Continuing Quest

WILLIAM DAVID SANSUM, M.D.
1880 - 1948

Continuing Quest

Dr. William David Sansum's Crusade against Diabetes

by Walker A. Tompkins

Published 1977 by
Sansum Medical Research Foundation
Santa Barbara, California

To my stepdaughter
DIANA ROSE WACHNER
and millions like her
who owe their lives
to diabetes research

BY WALKER A. TOMPKINS

Biography :

CONTINUING QUEST
(Dr. W. D. Sansum)

CALIFORNIA EDITOR
(Thomas M. Storke)

FOURTEEN AT THE TABLE
(Joseph Sexton)

LITTLE GIANT OF SIGNAL HILL
(Samuel B. Mosher)

Regional History:

IT HAPPENED IN OLD SANTA BARBARA

SANTA BARBARA PAST AND PRESENT

CALIFORNIA'S WONDERFUL CORNER

SANTA BARBARA'S ROYAL RANCHO

OLD SPANISH SANTA BARBARA

SANTA BARBARA YESTERDAYS

STEARNS WHARF CENTENNIAL

YANKEE BARBAREÑOS (MS)

GOLETA: THE GOOD LAND

MATTEI'S TAVERN

Table of Contents

Illustrations

THE EARLY YEARS, 1880 - 1930

THE LATER YEARS, 1931 - 1977

Foreword

Several years ago the late Mr. Harold S. Chase, Chairman of the Board of Directors of the Santa Barbara Cottage Hospital, and who for many years helped to shape the destiny of the hospital, urged me to document the history of Dr. William David Sansum's years as Director of the old Potter Metabolic Clinic.

Mr. Chase felt strongly that the story of the pioneer research and clinical work during the dramatic "insulin days" of the early 1920's, before and after the discovery of insulin by Drs. Frederick Banting and Charles H. Best in Toronto, would be of great interest to many individuals.

Doctor Sansum's happiest hours were spent in teaching patients, whether at the bedside or in the lecture room. He felt that he failed in his responsibility to patients unless he taught them how to care for their disorder, which is particularly true in the case of the diabetic because knowledge of management spells success or failure after returning home.

It was my good fortune to be closely associated with Doctor Sansum for nineteen years, during which time I was exposed to his philosophy of how to teach a person to lead a well-controlled and happy diabetic life. He taught patients to appreciate the importance of research for the benefit of mankind. In describing and defining research to his patients, Doctor Sansum would say, "Research is the study of diseases of unknown cause for which there is no satisfactory treatment known."

Because so little is known about diabetes with respect to the cause and complications, an increasing amount of research continues throughout the world with the result that interesting and significant bits of information come to light, providing encouragement for the diabetic patient and his physician.

Doctor Sansum's story is an important part of medical history in the United States. On the following pages Walker A. Tompkins, an experienced biographer and historian, has achieved an eminently successful portrayal of the life and work of William David Sansum, M.D.

Santa Barbara, California
September 1, 1977

H. I. BURTNESS, M.D.,
Chairman of the Board,
Sansum Medical Research Foundation

Acknowledgements

Continuing Quest is the story of a dedicated man of medicine and his lifelong struggle to find the cause and cure of diabetes mellitus. It was carpentered to be comprehensible to the layman without sacrificing technical details which would interest the diabetic patient, research technician, and physician.

Pitfalls await any lay writer who addresses himself to a subject as technical as metabolic diseases. He is dependent on professional sources of information. In the case of this book the writer is chiefly indebted to Mrs. Walter Painter of Santa Barbara, identified throughout this book by her maiden name, Ruth Bowden. She served as Dr. Sansum's head dietitian for the last 24 years of his life and remains today one of the Sansum family's closest friends and confidants. It was she who volunteered over the years to collect and store material of historical value pertaining to Dr. Sansum — his patients' records from the old Potter Metabolic

Clinic, half-century old annual reports issued by the Cottage Hospital, personal and professional correspondence, photographs, and other Sansum ephemera. This biography could never have been compiled at this late date without Ruth Bowden Painter's prior record-keeping and her painstaking and zealous cooperation at all stages of preparing the manuscript. She received valuable assistance from Mrs. Marjorie Coffin in typing extracts from publications.

While photographs from Dr. Sansum's boyhood are regrettably few, early-day pictures taken prior to his graduation from medical school in 1916 were generously provided by his niece, Mrs. Arthur G. Schrader of Antigo, Wisconsin. Another rich source of personal photographs was Dr. Sansum's son, Donald, and his wife Virginia Benson Sansum of Santa Barbara, who also supplied the doctor's personal scrapbook of press clippings dating from 1912. Other photo credits go to Dr. L. C. Maxwell of San Clemente, Mrs. Mildred Root Lewis, Dr. Doris McNamara, Mrs. Elizabeth Koehler Hastings, Mrs. Percival A. Gray, Dr. and Mrs. H. I. Burtness, the Vince Mandese photographs in the files of the Sansum Medical Research Foundation, Clarence Buggs' files at the Santa Barbara Cottage Hospital, and the Santa Barbara *News-Press*.

At the time the 46-year-old Sansum Clinic building was being vacated, prior to its demolition early in 1977 to make way for a parking lot, Dr. Burtness, board chairman of the Foundation, uncovered a forgotten treasure trove: Dr. Sansum's 55-year-old personal correspondence with E. F. Palmer of Louisville, Kentucky, and former patient Carl Klass of San Dimas, California. The doctor was a prolific letter writer and his voluminous files provided a virtual running diary of the tribulations suffered in the pioneer days of insulin research.

Friends and professional associates of Dr. Sansum

from the 1920's onward plumbed their memories to provide much of the fugitive material contained in the following pages. These included Barkley S. Wyckoff, D.M.D.; Doris E. McNamara, M.D.; Robert Sencerbox, R.Ph.; Melville Sahyun, Ph.D.; Loyal C. Maxwell, Ph.D.; Fritz Bischoff, Ph.D.; June Baker, R.N.; Mrs. Elsie Hill Johannsen; Mrs. Luella Burtness; Donald Sansum; Mrs. Virginia Benson Sansum; Mrs. Mildred Root Lewis, R.N.; Hildahl I. Burtness, M.D.; Elizabeth Buell; and Shirley Steelman.

The chapter dealing with the late Dr. Nathaniel Bowditch Potter is based on his 1930 biography "The Victor" by Charles Henry Brent.

Finis Haskins, curator of the Goleta Valley Historical Society, graciously checked out the chains of title for all Santa Barbara properties owned by Dr. Sansum during his lifetime, including his various homes, the Isla Vista beach house, and the Sansum Clinic.

The manuscript was checked in whole or in part for technical and historical accuracy by many experts, including Dr. and Mrs. Burtness, Mrs. Ruth Bowden Painter, Dr. Loyal C. Maxwell, Drs. Francis and Marianna Masin, Dr. Casimir Domz, Robert E. Bason, Dr. Donald E. McMillan, and Dr. Doris E. McNamara.

Current statistical material compiled by the American Diabetes Association was supplied through the courtesy of Mrs. Walter D. (Gloria) Merrigan, Jr. of Goleta, a board member of the ADA's Southern California Affiliate. Clarence Buggs, archivist, and Rodney J. Lamb, administrator, of the Cottage Hospital were most helpful, as was Mrs. Kevin Fay of the David L. Reeves Medical Library.

The book jacket features the bronze bust of Dr. Sansum executed in 1950 by sculptors Holger and Helen Webster Jensen of Santa Monica. Professional editorial assistance was provided by my wife, Barbara Hathaway

Tompkins. The author also acknowledges the coopera-
tion of Daniel Turner, trustee, and Arlene Adams and
Deborah J. Shaw, amanuenses at the Sansum Medical
Research Foundation; and manager Glenn Fricke and
Sharon Talbot of Schauer Printing Company.

Most of the verbatim quotes attributed to Dr.
Sansum in this book came directly from his own
writings, including technical reports, or the reminis-
cences of his relatives and friends, who were unanimous
in saying their lives had been enriched by their contacts
with such a dedicated and distinguished physician.

Santa Barbara, California
July 10, 1977

—WALKER A. TOMPKINS

1

An Invitation
from Santa Barbara

In the bucolic village that was Baraboo, Wisconsin
in 1890, most of the barefoot boys of ten-goin'-on-'leven
nourished aspirations to become circus clowns or
locomotive engineers. But Willie Sansum had different
ideas.

"When I grow up," he boasted, "I'm gonna be a
doctor!"

Such a weird ambition was incomprehensible to
Willie's peers. Baraboo was both the winter head-
quarters of the Ringling Brothers Circus and a division
point on the Chicago & North Western Railroad. What
more glamour could life offer a red-blooded American
boy than flying on a trapeze or cracking a throttle like
Casey Jones?

No clue appears in the Sansum family archives to
explain Willie's all-consuming interest in a medical
career at such a tender age. Perhaps it stemmed from
youthful hero-worship of the town's lone horse-and-

buggy doctor. Whatever his motivation, Willie's precocious choice of a profession enabled him to beam his education in a laser-straight direction without dissipating precious years on scholastic detours.

Baraboo in the 1880s was a halcyon small town, archetypal of heartland America. Mark Twain could well have used it as the setting for Tom Sawyer's adventures. It is located on a bend of the Baraboo River, ten miles south of the scenic Wisconsin Dells and an hour's drive northwest of the state capitol, Madison.

Willie's parents were English. Elizabeth Frisby was born in 1851 in Bristol; David Sansum was born in Stroud, Gloustershire, in 1850. They emigrated to the Wisconsin frontier in their twenties, married, and settled in Baraboo in 1874. William David Sansum, born September 25, 1880, was the third child in a family of four boys and four girls.

A niece, Mrs. Arthur G. Schrader of Antigo, Wisconsin, recalls that the Sansum family lived modestly in a large, baywindowed saltbox house on a thirty-acre dairy and truck garden farm near the Baraboo River. "Willie's father had a greenhouse," Mrs. Schrader said, "the rear of which was blanketed with hops which he sold to home brewers in the community. Mrs. Sansum sold yeast by the cupful to the bread makers."

One of Willie's boyhood recollections was of the deep well in the front yard, where milk from the family's herd of four cows was stored in cans and lowered into the cold water. Mother Sansum made her pin money selling milk to the neighbors, who would come to the house every morning with their shiny tin buckets.

Willie's aspirations to enter the medical profession in adulthood in no way curtailed his growing up as a normal midwestern boy. He early plumbed the depths of bliss to be had from a willow pole, a bit of string, a

2

cork bobber and a bent pin fishhook. The Baraboo River was an ideal fishing stream, teeming with ten-inch bullheads, sunfish and bluegills, and an occasional wall-eyed pike. Willie Sansum was to indulge his piscatorial hobby to the end of his days, well knowing the therapeutic benefits to be found at the butt end of a fishing rod.

An unusual lifelong hobby he picked up as a child in Wisconsin was that of knitting. The frugal Mother Sansum taught all eight of her brood the art of knitting and purling, so they could make their own stockings, sweaters, mufflers and mittens. In adult life, Sansum did most of his profound thinking to the accompaniment of clicking needles.

The product of a God-fearing Protestant family, Willie dutifully attended Sunday School and "preaching" at a small frame church on the outskirts of town. In his teens he officially affiliated with the Congregational Church, largely because his best girl, Mabel Drew, worshipped with that denomination.

Willie learned his three Rs at the Lyons Common School on the edge of town, consistently making the scholastic honor roll and receiving a diploma dated February 28, 1895. He graduated from Baraboo High School with the Class of '00, having filled out physically to where he could discourage any "sissy" jibes from his peers about his knitting. At this point he also shed the "Willie" diminutive and became Will.

Financially Will was now on his own. He got a job as a section hand on the Chicago and North Western Railroad, the income from which enabled him to enroll in the two-year Wisconsin State Normal School at Stevens Point in Portage County, some seventy miles north of his native Sauk County. While there he went out for football and qualified for the varsity squad.

Armed with a teaching certificate in 1903, Will obtained a position in the public school system at New

Richmond, in the northwestern part of Wisconsin. Still waiting back home was his childhood sweetheart, Mabel Barbara Drew, born to Wisconsin pioneers on July 31, 1884 in Baraboo. They were married on her twenty-second birthday in 1906. After a short honeymoon in Minneapolis, they returned to New Richmond where Will resumed his teaching, his bride taking in boarders to augment her husband's medical education fund. Fortunately a scholarship enabled Will to quit teaching in 1910 and enroll in the University of Wisconsin in Madison. There he took his Bachelor of Science degree in 1912. Then, at age 32 — a decade behind most of his peers — William David Sansum at last achieved his golden dream and enrolled in the prestigious Rush Medical College in Chicago as a Fellow of the Otho S. A. Sprague Memorial Institute. The college had been named for Dr. Benjamin Rush, one of the signers of the Declaration of Independence.

Both Will and Mabel wanted children. Since his wife was now approaching thirty, it was deemed time to start a family, even though he was still in school. Mabel carried two pregnancies to full term, only to have her babies stillborn because of toxemia. Advised by obstetricians that Mabel probably would never be able to bear a child, the Sansums found parental fullfillment by adopting a nine-month-old boy in December 1914, whom they christened Donald Roger Sansum.

"We had gone to the adoption agency in Chicago with every intention of bringing home a girl," the Sansums enjoyed telling friends, "but when we saw cute little Donal — we added the 'd' later — his gurgling and laughing just won our hearts forever."

During his crowded undergraduate years at Rush Medical College Will worked in the Sprague Institute Laboratories doing experimental research on dogs. Here he showed the first bright promise of becoming one of the nation's most respected medical research scientists. It was during this formative period of his professional career that he elected to focus his research on a virtual *terra incognita* of medicine, the metabolic diseases of man.

At the time Sansum first became interested in diabetes mellitus, any diagnosis of that disease was tantamount to a death sentence. At best, life could only be prolonged a few months through rigid diets which offered little in the way of physical well-being or opportunity to be economically useful to society. In choosing diabetes as the subject of his doctoral thesis at Rush, Sansum was choosing his lifelong occupation — a continuing quest to find how to cure, and prevent, diabetes mellitus.

The history of the disease proved a fascinating subject to young Sansum in medical school. A papyrus found in Luxor, Egypt, dating to 1500 B.C., contained a medical prescription for alleviating polyuria, or excessive urination, which was the earliest recorded reference to a classic symptom of diabetes. The disease was first described in detail in 30 B.C. by Aurelius Celsus, the chief medical scribe of ancient Rome, who reported that the as-yet unnamed ailment was not contagious, was probably hereditary, and was invariably fatal. Celsus outlined the basic symptoms of diabetes for the first time in medical history: excessive thirst, excessive urination, abnormal hunger, progressive loss of weight, and a tendency toward slow healing of wounds and gangrene.

A generation later, Aretaeus of Cappadocia, a renowned Ionian Greek physician and scholar second only to the immortal Hippocrates, attached a label to the mystery killer: *diabetes*, from a Greek word meaning "to run through" or "to siphon."

For the next sixteen hundred years, the scourge of

5

diabetes continued to baffle men of medicine. Then, in 1775, an English clinician named Thomas Willis observed the sweetness and honeylike nature of diabetic urine. He added a descriptive adjective to Aretaeus' label, *mellitus*, from the Latin noun *mell*, meaning honey.

Another century passed before Matthew Dobson reported the sweetness of blood serum in victims of diabetes mellitus, and the presence of sugar in their urine. In 1788, Thomas Cawley reported that post mortem analyses of diabetic pancreases showed marked pathological changes in that organ. This was a breakthrough, the first time that diabetes was linked to the pancreatic function.

Still another hundred years elapsed, with meager or no gains on the front of diabetic research. Chemists discovered acetone in the urine of diabetics compara- tively recently — in 1875, which was only five years before Sansum was born. He was four years old when Kuelz and Oscar Minkowski first identified beta- hydroxybutyric acid as a constituent of diabetic urine. This acid was a product of incomplete combustion of fat in the body, a condition always obtained when an excessive amount of fat was burned with an inadequate amount of sugar.

During Sansum's preparatory years at Rush, he eagerly devoured every morsel of published information he could find about man's efforts to conquer diabetes. Death from the disease, scientists had determined, was usually due to an accumulation of toxic acids in the body to produce the condition known as diabetic coma, first described by the British clinician Prout in 1884.

In 1889, Sansum learned, Minkowski and Von Mering demonstrated that the removal of the pancreas from a dog resulted in an elevation of the blood sugar and the excretion of large amounts of sugar in the urine. This discovery was vastly important, for the canine diabetes closely matched conditions found in human sufferers, thus definitely suggesting a faulty functioning of the pancreas as contributing to the disease. Another significant breakthrough in the crusade against diabetes occurred in 1901 when E. L. Opie isolated the portion of the pancreas which seemed to be most vulnerable to the disease — the several million microscopic nodules which differed from the rest of the pancreas's cellular structure, although amounting to only three percent of the organ's weight.

These nodules are called the islands, or islets of Langerhans, after Dr. Paul Langerhans, the German pathologist who first described them in 1869. Examinations of the pancreases of persons who had died of diabetes showed Opie that their islands of Langerhans had degenerated to a greater degree than the rest of the pancreas, the organ responsible for manufacturing digestive secretions which enter the small intestine through a duct system.

Here, at last, was specific progress. Once the islands of Langerhans had been identified as having a link to diabetes, attention could be focussed on finding means to manage the disease, and eventually prevent diabetes from occurring at all.

Kuelz was the first advocate of carefully-controlled diets based on individual tolerances and the number of calories needed by a diabetic patient. Kuelz's early treatments called for partial starvation, usually limiting the amount of carbohydrates to the amount the patient's system could burn. To build up the caloric count, these diets tended to run heavily to fats.

At the time Dr. Sansum first thought seriously of entering the field of diabetic research, the direction of study was just turning to the possibility of extracting substances from the pancreases of animals which, if properly refined, might be injected into human tissue to compensate for the patient's insufficiency of pancreatic output. In theory, at least, the patient might then be able to handle his own sugar metabolism. So far, science had not been able to accomplish this. Later research proved they were on the wrong track.

Such was the background of what medicine had been attempting to achieve, with only minimal success, in the centuries since diabetes mellitus had been identified and named, long before Christ walked the earth. Joining this army of scientists dedicated to finding the answer to the cure and prevention of diabetes brought to William David Sansum an overwhelming awareness of being part of a grand continuing quest; it grew and intensified until it became the all-pervasive obsession and ultimate goal of his life.

On June 30, 1916, when Sansum was in his thirty-fifth year — an age when most young doctors were well settled in their practices — William David Sansum received the degree of *Medicinae Doctor cum laude* from Rush Medical College. His doctoral thesis was titled "Studies on the Theory of Diabetes Mellitus," and it challenged some of the pet theories of the day. Newspaper reports stated that one of the sections of Sansum's thesis was "most important from a scientific standpoint," concerning a rare sugar that had never been prepared in its pure state, the cost of producing the first ounce in the laboratory amounting to nearly $2,000.

"Dr. Sansum's experiments also included a test of ordinary corn syrup," news releases said, "which proved that the value of corn syrup is only slightly less than the purest glucose doctors could buy. This report is so pleasing to the manufacturers of corn syrup that Dr. Sansum was asked to publish the work." Also noted was the fact that Dr. Sansum described the "smallest pump in the world," used in the study of intravenous feeding.

Dr. Sansum began his internship at the

Presbyterian Hospital in Chicago under the well-known American specialist in metabolic research, Dr. Roland T. Woodyatt. When the United States declared war on Germany two years later, Dr. Woodyatt was called into the Army Medical Corps for overseas duty. He turned over his laboratory operations, and some of his lecturing schedule at Rush, to his star apprentice, Dr. W. D. Sansum.

Assuming he had found his permanent life's work in Chicago, Dr. Sansum moved Mabel and son Donald to a comfortable home in suburban Evanston and settled down to his duties in the belief he would spend the rest of his life there.

When Dr. Woodyatt returned from the war in 1919 he found that his erstwhile assistant had made such giant strides in metabolic research, especially the relationship of controlled diets to diabetes, that the apprentice's reputation threatened to outshine the master's. For his part, Dr. Sansum found his research and collegiate-level lecturing afforded him the happiest and most fulfilling years of his life to date. His publications in learned journals were winning international attention on a variety of abstruse subjects, such as extrasystoles in the mammalian heart due to the stimulation of the Keith Flack node; studies on the theory of diabetes involving glycolic aldehyde in phlorhizinized dogs; a study of narcotic drugs in phlorhizin diabetes; the food value of commercial glucose; the behavior of d-l-glyceric aldehyde in the normal and diabetic organism — just to name a few.

Between 1917 and 1920, Dr. Sansum's by-line appeared in no less than seventeen major scholarly papers, a publication record without equal among his peers, climaxed by a booklet published July 1, 1918, which broke records for long titles: *"The Treatment of Diabetes Mellitus, a Brief Outline on the Management of Typical Moderately-severe Cases of the Disease, for*

9

the Use of Patients, Social Workers, Students and Physicians in the Central Free Dispensary, Rush Medical College, Chicago."

If it did nothing else, the publication established W. D. Sansum, M.D. high in the ranks of American diabetes specialists.

He was riding the crest of his Chicago career when, almost unnoticed, his fortieth birthday arrived on September 25, 1920. As if fate were punctuating that milestone date, Dr. Sansum received a letter which was to create a hinge-point in his destiny.

The letter was postmarked "Santa Barbara, California." It was from George Owen Knapp, a name Sansum recognized as that of the multimillionaire president and founder of the Union Carbide Company, one of the nation's great corporations. What reason, Dr. Sansum wondered aloud, could such a titan of the industrial world have in writing him a letter from the west coast and marking it "Personal and confidential"?

"Why not open it and see, dear?" suggested his wife.

As he read the letter from California, a puzzled frown put its notch between Dr. Sansum's brows. Looking up, he said, "Mr. Knapp is writing me in his capacity as a member of the board of the Santa Barbara Cottage Hospital. He wants to meet with me to discuss my becoming the director of the hospital's metabolic clinic — the one founded by Dr. Nathaniel Bowditch Potter!"

2

The Potter Metabolic Clinic

The name of Dr. Nathaniel Bowditch Potter was well known to Dr. Sansum, as indeed it was to the entire world of medicine. He was born on Christmas Day 1869 in Keeseville, New York; and by the time the U.S. entered World War I in 1917 he was recognized as one of the foremost diagnosticians in the world in the field of metabolic medicine.

Like Dr. Sansum, he had set his sights on becoming a physician while still a child. He took his Bachelor of Arts degree at the College of the City of New York in 1888, another B.A. at Harvard in 1890. His graduation from Harvard Medical School in 1894 was followed by a period of study in Vienna, the world center of medicine.

Dr. Potter married Mary Sargent in Brookline, Massachusetts, in 1908. But instead of embracing the promise of an easy and lucrative practice in Boston, where he had high social standing, Dr. Potter chose to pursue his research activities in competitive New York, concentrating on three metabolic diseases, diabetes mellitus, gout, and nephritis.

Dr. Potter's succinct definition of "metabolism" was universally memorized by medical students of the period:

"The body in reality is a great complex chemical laboratory in which Nature is constantly destroying old and building up new tissues, from the moment of birth to the instant of death. These changes are essentially chemical, and can be more or less perfectly studied and measured.

"Disease, from whatever cause, alters the chemistry of the body. Many diseases are essentially chemical in both cause and result. It is impossible to correctly interpret any disease without studying the chemistry of the body. Some of the most important diseases affecting man are purely chemical in nature; no other line of investigation affords information as to their nature. The general phenomena of building up the body and disposing of the worn-out materials is known as METABOLISM."

Shortly after the birth of his second daughter in 1911, Dr. Potter's personal physician confirmed what the patient already knew: he himself was a victim of diabetes, with advanced complications. Taking such precautions as were then deemed necessary, Dr. Potter labored on in silence, no one except his wife knowing of the presence of the fatal illness, which became progressively worse.

In September 1915 he wrote a friend in England, "I have been quite ill, the nature, degree and knowledge of my illness I am still concealing from as large a portion of my world as possible, in the hopes of prolonging and still utilizing the efficiency which remains in me."

Dr. Potter was well aware of the irreversible nature of his illness. He had the spiritual fortitude to accept that fact. But he was not prepared to weather a blow which came in 1915 when his beloved youngest daughter, Mary, contracted a rare form of leukemia. She became a *cause célébre* among a veritable army of Dr. Potter's professional colleagues, but she died despite their massive efforts to save her life.

As a monument to Mary Robeson Potter, in 1916 Dr. Potter founded, with financial aid from the Carnegie Corporation and other subscribers, a "Memorial Laboratory and Clinic for the Study and Treatment of Nephritis, Gout and Diabetes." The clinic was based at New York City Hospital and included what Dr. Potter described as "a very complete laboratory with chemist, assistant chemist, clinical assistant and dietitians for the accurate and intensive study of metabolic patients."

An epidemic of infantile paralysis hit New York in the latter half of 1916, and an acute shortage of supplies and equipment unavoidably postponed the opening of the clinic until February 1, 1917, but Dr. Potter considered the work "well organized and in efficient operational order" by May. Personnel were receiving specialized technical training at the Rockefeller Institute Hospital, with Carnegie providing the money to equip the laboratory.

At this time Dr. Potter stood at the apex of his brilliant professional career. He was a professor of clinical medicine at Columbia University's College of Physicians and Surgeons; a visiting physician to the New York City Hospital; chief of the medical division of St. Mark's Hospital; consulting physician to the French Hospital, the New York Throat, Nose and Lung Hospital, and the Central Islip State Hospital; and at one time was the only American member of the Sociètè Médicale des Hòspitaux de Paris.

But at age 47, when he should have been in his physical prime, Dr. Potter felt the vise-jaws of ill health crushing in remorselessly. Not only was he an incurable diabetic; he was approaching the terminal phases of nephritis, heart disease, and tuberculosis.

His doctors advised that another cold winter in New York City would kill him. They recommended moving to a more salubrious climate without delay, and urged that he retire from his profession.

Dr. Potter accepted the inevitable, but foremost in his mind was seeing his fledgling clinic through its infancy. It was already beginning to lose staff personnel to the armed forces, once the United States entered the war against the Kaiser's Germany.

Would the Carnegie Corporation and his other sponsors consent to transferring their financial subsidies from New York to some other locale, perhaps far away? Prompt assurances were forthcoming from the president of the Carnegie Corporation, Dr. Henry Pritchett, who told Dr. Potter that a mere shift in geography would in no way jeopardize funding the research clinic.

Thus reassured, Dr. Potter went through the agony of resigning his numerous professional posts in the East. He elected to move his clinic to the sunny shores of Southern California — specifically, to the sleepy little town of Santa Barbara, population 18,000, located on the coast ninety miles north of Los Angeles.

Dr. Potter's selection of Santa Barbara for his new base of operations was probably influenced in part by the town's existing image as a health center, a reputation which had budded midway through the Nineteenth Century, reaching full flower in the 1890s. The fact that Andrew Carnegie and John D. Rockefeller, Sr. had enjoyed winter vacations in beautiful Santa Barbara was also a factor in directing Dr. Potter's attention 2,500 miles west of Manhattan rather than to sunny climes such as Florida or Texas.

Santa Barbara's several mineral and hot springs had been popular as health spas among the prehistoric

Indians and the gray-robed Franciscan friars who had established the tenth in their string of twenty-one California missions at Santa Barbara in 1786. Scorbutic sailors of the seven seas had spread the word that they could heal the skin lesions caused by their scurvy in the sulphur mud baths of Spanish Santa Barbara.

In the late 1860s, a Yankee physician, Samuel B. Brinkerhoff, settled in Santa Barbara. What he termed "the oleagenous fumes wafting on the sea breezes" off Santa Barbara's perpetual floating oil slicks, fed by submarine petroleum springs, were, Brinkerhoff suggested, curative for visitors with respiratory ailments.

A gullible public took Dr. Brinkerhoff at his word. Soon health-seekers began pouring into Santa Barbara by coastal steamer and stagecoach. Most of them quickly regained their health in Santa Barbara's balmy year-around climate, whether or not they inhaled a single breath of Dr. Brinkerhoff's oleagenous fumes off the ocean.

Eastern newspapers began referring to Santa Barbara, California as a "sanatorium city," causing local editors to grumble that their home town was turning into a Mecca for the moribund, and pointing out that Santa Barbara boasted other assets than its climate, such as incomparable Mediterranean-type mountain and marine scenery.

With fresh hordes of health-seekers arriving on every stage and steamer, local entrepreneurs hastily built hotels and boarding houses to accommodate the influx, but it was not until 1888, a year after the first railroad train reached Santa Barbara, that the community recognized a pressing need for a good hospital.

Led by a wealthy Montecito matriarch named Mary A. Ashley, fifty women of the town filed articles of incorporation for the "Santa Barbara Cottage

Hospital" and launched a fund-raising campaign to erect a cottage-style facility in which each department — medical, surgical, obstetrical, pharmaceutical, etc. — would occupy a separate bungalow. The site chosen for the future hospital was the block bounded by Bath, Third (Pueblo), Castillo and Fourth (Junipero) Streets, a location then far out in the country, removed from the dust and noise of downtown.

After three years it became evident that sufficient funds for a cottage-type hospital could not be raised in such a small community, so a compromise was reached and a single three-story redwood structure was built at the corner of Castillo and Junipero Streets.

It opened in 1891, retaining the cozy name of "Cottage Hospital."

Ten years later the Southern Pacific Railroad, after a fourteen-year delay, completed its Coast Line through Santa Barbara, linking San Francisco and Los Angeles. This event opened the floodgates of a new immigration boom for Santa Barbara. A Los Angeles hotel magnate, Milo M. Potter (no kin of Dr. Potter's) erected a $1,500,000, six-story, 600-room luxury hotel overlooking West Beach between Bath and Chapala Streets, staging his grand opening in 1902.

The character of Santa Barbara visitors underwent an abrupt and not-so-subtle change. Instead of health seekers, the Potter Hotel attracted elite pleasure-seekers — the likes of the Rockefellers, Carnegies, Astors, Vanderbilts, Armours, Fleischmanns, Cudahys — the social *haut monde* of the Eastern seaboard, the jet set of their day.

Many millionaires who were introduced to Santa Barbara through holidays spent at the Potter Hotel — Chicago's George Owen Knapp was one of them — remained to build marble mansions on world-famous wooded estates in Montecito, Santa Barbara's eastern suburb. These winter-dwellers, "hill barons" as they were called, began pouring vast amounts of money into philanthropic enterprises such as the Santa Barbara Cottage Hospital.

Such was the favorable situation which existed in Santa Barbara when Dr. Potter arrived in the autumn of 1917, a sick man, indeed a dying man. His superlative reputation had preceded him across the continent, and he found the directors of Cottage Hospital open and receptive to integrating Potter's metabolic clinic into their facilities, even before Dr. Potter's arrival on the scene.

Out of this camaraderie evolved a formal working agreement between Dr. Potter and the Santa Barbara Cottage Hospital. The hospital agreed to furnish private rooms for Potter patients at regular prices. Five beds would be set aside for Santa Barbara residents having little or no means. A complete diet kitchen, with Dr. Potter to provide any special utensils and dishes his work might require, was available to him. So was the use of hospital laboratory equipment, if he supplied any specialized or extra equipment pertinent to his metabolic research, including such expendables as chemicals. The hospital would provide charts, heat, light and cleaning service for clinic-connected wards, kitchen and laboratory; and meals for certain clinic staff personnel.

Dr. Potter agreed to furnish and pay the salary of Bertha Conboy, the dietitian-nurse he had brought out from New York, and furnish her outside living quarters. He would also provide a chemist, assistant chemist and clinical assistants, and pay half the salary of the hospital's laboratory technician engaged in clinic-connected work. Any extra charts or printed forms, and the medical supervision of clinic patients, would also be Dr. Potter's responsibility under the joint agreement.

Changing the locus of Dr. Potter's work from New York to Santa Barbara generated news items in the medical journals. At Harvard University, the *Graduates' Magazine* reported proudly on their alumnus, "Dr. Potter moved to Santa Barbara, carrying his indomitable courage with him. With the consent of the subscribers, the funds for the laboratory work which he inaugurated in New York were transferred to and affiliated with the Cottage Hospital of Santa Barbara . . . He organized the work, presided over and inspired it, triumphing over, in the spirit, a relentless malady."

Potter's biographer, Charles Henry Brent, wrote from the American Embassy in London a decade later, "The transfer of the Potter Clinic from New York to its California home was an admirable move. Santa Barbara was the most favorable climate for Dr. Potter, and well-situated for the purpose of a metabolic clinic. Its equable climate and beautiful scenery, combining both sea and mountains, make it an earthly paradise.

"A chronic patient in this all-year-round climate leads an outdoor life without danger of respiratory or other infections, which are the immediate cause of the deaths of the majority of those suffering from metabolic diseases that have become chronic. It is also probable that the mental quiet necessary for these difficult studies is more likely to be obtained in a smaller community, rather than in the large urban centers.

"From the point of view of the patient, the location of the clinic in a place free from great extremes of temperature, permitting an open air life twelve months of the year, and free also from the social stresses of metropolitan life, is a condition most favorable to success."

Despite the handicaps caused by his debilitating illnesses and decreasing strength, Dr. Potter got his transplanted memorial clinic off to a vigorous start in Santa Barbara.

"I was extremely fortunate," Dr. Potter wrote, "in

securing the services of two competent, well-trained clinical assistants, Drs. Hilmar O. Koefod and J. J. O'Donnell, both of whom had been obliged to resign from their war activities and seek Santa Barbara's favorable climate on account of their own condition."

The new Potter Metabolic Clinic began receiving patients referred by physicians from coast to coast, at a rate more than sufficient to be handled by the limited facilities and staff.

"We are studying and treating them in the same careful way as the New York City Hospital," Dr. Potter told a colleague in the east, "with the additional advantages of adequate accommodations in Cottage Hospital for private as well as charity patients, and of a climate ideal for the treatment of sufferers from diabetes, nephritis or gout. The limited space in the laboratory and diet kitchen, in comparison to the rapidly increasing numbers of applicants for admission to the service; the distance from centers of supplies and equipment; and growing difficulties inherent to wartime conditions, are now the only stumbling blocks to our progress."

On July 1, 1918, the chief of clinic, Dr. Koefod, reported to the hospital board: "The average length of stay at the hospital for diabetics has been 34.5 days, and for the nephritics, 14.7 days. The length of time consumed in rendering diabetics free of sugar through dieting has averaged eight days. The total hospital days for clinic patients number 823."

In order to brief west coast physicians on his work and methods, although more dead than alive, Dr. Potter visited Los Angeles and addressed 250 members of the Los Angeles County Medical Society on the fasting treatment he used in diabetes. On December 7 he appeared before the Southern California Physicians Group to discuss the pitfalls of diagnosing syphilis. The following spring, with his health showing a slight

19

improvement due to the Santa Barbara climate, Dr. Potter addressed the California Academy of Medicine in San Francisco and the California State Medical Society at Del Monte.

But the ravages of ill health eventually made it impossible for Dr. Potter to walk, even with the aid of crutches. In spite of his crippling weakness, he continued to carry on his daily routine. He had to be lifted from his bed and carried to his car to be driven to Cottage Hospital, where he made his rounds in a wheelchair.

When he got too weak to sit up in a wheelchair, Dr. Potter ordered selected patients brought to his hospital room, where they came under the healing influence of his fortitude, described by one admirer as being "like radium, constantly throwing off emanations, without seemingly wasting the source of supply."

Visitors remarked on the appropriateness of a framed scroll mounted above the fireplace mantle in the clinic lobby, which carried the familiar, inspiring lines by Kipling:

> *If you can force your heart and nerve*
> *and sinew*
> *To serve your turn long after they are*
> *gone*
> *And so hold on when there is nothing*
> *in you*
> *Except the will which says to them*
> *"Hold on" . . .*

Such fortitude in the face of mounting pain and debility made a profound impression on a trio of wealthy Santa Barbarans, George Owen Knapp, founder of Union Carbide; C.K.G. Billings, a director of Knapp's company; and Frederick Forest Peabody of Cluett, Peabody & Company, makers of Arrow shirts and collars. These three friends owned huge estates in Montecito, and had contributed heavily to Cottage

Hospital in recent years.

On August 30, 1918, the trio announced through the columns of the Santa Barbara newspapers that "the finest laboratory and clinic for research work in medicine and surgery will be built at Cottage Hospital and named the Potter Metabolic Wing."

The new wing would alleviate the cramped conditions which were impeding Dr. Potter's work. Architect Winsor Soule was engaged to draw up the plans under Dr. Potter's supervision. Contractors Johnson & Avery were soon staking out the foundations for the new wing, which jutted out from the central hospital building's southwest corner, bisecting the angle of the intersection of Pueblo and Castillo Streets.

The building, two stories in height with bedrooms occupying the upper floor and laboratories at ground level, got under way on April 13, 1919, although Dr. Potter was too ill to leave his bed for the ground-breaking ceremonies on that date.

By June the clinic was only half completed. The stricken man consented to leave his work long enough for a vacation at Lake Tahoe, where it was hoped the altitude, 6,275 feet above sea level, the pine-scented mountain air, and relief from his clinic duties might rally Dr. Potter's flagging strength.

When he was driven to the Chapala Street railroad station and his stretcher placed aboard a Pullman for San Francisco, his grieving colleagues shared an unvoiced premonition that they would not see Dr. Potter again.

He was destined never to reach Lake Tahoe. Upon arrival in San Francisco, Dr. Potter was taken to St. Francis Hospital for an "extended period of rest" before resuming his journey. Even so, Dr. Potter summoned a secretary and a laboratory technician and by superhuman effort, pushed to completion a series of technical papers he had been working on for ten years.

Twenty-four hours after finishing that monumental task Dr. Potter performed his last conscious act, the selection of a motto for the book plate for his library books, "Patience, Accuracy, Vision." "Because after all," he whispered to his attending nurse, "has not the object of my life been to bring science and humanity together?"

Dr. Potter then lapsed into a diabetic coma which caused his death on July 5, 1919, midway through his forty-ninth year. He left instructions forbidding a formal funeral service, saying he did not wish his busy friends and co-workers to be taken away from more important matters by such a melancholy ritual. He requested his beloved wife to accompany his body to the family cemetery in Woods Hole, Massachusetts, and to bury him beside their little daughter Mary, in whose memory the metabolic clinic had been established.

Although the news of Dr. Potter's death had been anticipated for weeks in Santa Barbara, members of his staff still reacted with stunned disbelief. Flags flew at half-staff at Cottage Hospital, the county courthouse, and city hall, as Santa Barbara paid last respects to its recently adopted son.

At the Memorial Clinic, shortly to be renamed the Potter Metabolic Clinic of Santa Barbara Cottage Hospital, the daily work had to go on. At the time their director died, the charter staff was as follows:

Chief of clinic, Hilmar M. Koefod, M.D. Research worker, Inez Smith, M.A. Chief chemist, Elisabetta C. Pennell, M.S. Assistant chemist, Evelyn M. Warren. Pathologist and bacteriologist, Adelle Snyder. Dietitian-nurse, Bertha C. Conboy; assistant, A. Blanche Catudal. Secretary and accountant, Laura E. Shumard. Chartist and assistant accountant, Julia A. Haynes. Historian and assistant secretary, Adelaide E. Flint. Librarian and abstractor, Felicia Robbins, M.D.

The charter advisory council consisted of Theobald Smith, M.D., LL.D., Princeton University; Henry S.

Pritchett LL.D., Carnegie Corporation; Donald D. Van Slyke, M.D., Alfred E. Cohn, M.D. and Edgar Stillman, M.D., all of Rockefeller Institute Hospital; and August Hoch, M.D., consulting psychopathologist.

Dr. N.W. Janney, a Boston diabetes specialist, was named acting director of the clinic, to serve until a permanent replacement for Dr. Potter could be found. It was Dr. Janney who presided over the formal opening of the new Potter Metabolic Wing on October 25, 1919.

The chief of staff of Cottage Hospital was Dr. Franklin R. Nuzum, a former tuberculosis patient who had come to Santa Barbara as George Owen Knapp's personal physician. Dr. Nuzum was a graduate of the University of Chicago and Rush Medical College and had served his residency at the Presbyterian Hospital in Chicago where he was a close associate of Dr. Woodyatt's. It was through this connection that Dr. Nuzum knew of the fine work in diabetes research being done by Dr. Woodyatt's present assistant, Dr. William D. Sansum.

"In my opinion," Dr. Nuzum told the Cottage Hospital trustees, "Dr. Sansum is the best qualified man in the country to step into Dr. Potter's shoes. Providing, of course, that he is willing to accept a position in Santa Barbara."

In September 1920, hospital director George Owen Knapp followed Dr. Nuzum's recommendation and wrote to Dr. Sansum requesting an interview in Chicago. The day he received Dr. Sansum's approval for such a meeting, Knapp boarded a fast train for Chicago.

3

Dr. Sansum
Takes the Helm

A personal rapport which followed both men to the end of their lives sprang full-blown the instant George Owen Knapp, the industrial tycoon, clasped hands with Dr. William D. Sansum, the diabetes researcher, on a fateful morning in September 1920 in the lobby of Chicago's Blackstone Hotel.

On their way up to Knapp's suite, he came straight to the point: Dr. Potter, after moving west for his health, had died and the board of trustees of Cottage Hospital were desirous of having Dr. Sansum fill the job of director of Potter's clinic.

"We are fully aware," Knapp continued, "that you are engrossed in important metabolic work here at Presbyterian Hospital with Dr. Woodyatt. We realize you and your family have settled in a new home in Evanston and might be reluctant to uproot yourselves from your circle of old friends and professional associates. On the other hand, you might find exciting new challenges and opportunities in Santa Barbara, Doctor. As a Chicagoan myself, I can heartily endorse Santa Barbara as a place to live and bring up a family amid beautiful surroundings. Such a move might actually prove to be advantageous both to your professional career and in a broader sense, the advancement of scientific knowledge. We are prepared to pay you a salary of $500 a month, plus a guarantee of an additional $500 from your private practice, plus free office space and other fringe benefits."

A thousand dollars a month might seem ridiculously low in the 1970s, when many blue-collar laborers made that much. But in California in the 1920s, it was a princely stipend, commensurate with the honor and the responsibility the position involved.

Dr. Sansum did not commit himself. "I will seriously discuss your proposal with my wife," he said, "and wire you my decision as soon as I have reached it. I feel honored by your trust."

On that inconclusive note, the two parted. Knapp, hardly daring to be hopeful, returned to Santa Barbara. Before the week was out he received a telegram from Dr. Sansum:

> AM PLEASED TO ACCEPT DIRECTORSHIP OF POTTER METABOLIC CLINIC STOP WILL COME WEST SOON AS CAN WIND UP FAMILY AND PROFESSIONAL AFFAIRS. SANSUM.

Patients' records of the Potter Metabolic Clinic show that at four o'clock on the afternoon of Monday, November 8, 1920, a patient named Charles E. Cowan, age 51, of Anaheim, California, was admitted for treatment of an advanced case of diabetic acidosis, whose prognosis permitted virtually no hope. All unknowing, Cowan was to write a footnote in medical history books, along with his attending physician, W. D. Sansum.

At the very hour that Cowan was being booked by the admissions office at Cottage Hospital's Potter Wing, a group led by the hospital's chief of staff, Dr. Nuzum, was down at the Chapala Street railway depot to meet a train which was bringing Dr. and Mrs. William David Sansum and their six-year-old son, Donald, to Santa Barbara.

Recalling that event fifty-seven years later, Donald Sansum said, "When we had boarded the Overland Limited in Chicago three days earlier, the weather off Lake Michigan was near freezing under leaden skies which threatened snow. What a contrast we found in Santa Barbara, basking in the sunlight of Indian summer! I will never forget seeing my first palm trees, roses and geraniums blooming on all sides, a cloudless blue sky over the mountain range behind the city. All that and the Pacific Ocean, the Channel Islands lying on the south horizon — you have no idea the visual impact all this beauty had on newcomers from Chicago. We became 'instant Barbareños!'"

Dr. Sansum's first words to his welcoming committee were "You folks have any fishing around here?"

"River? Lake? Surf? Wharf? Deep-sea?" Dr. Nuzum inquired over their handshake. "Fishermen have a choice here in Santa Barbara."

Amid the laughter, Mabel Sansum chided her husband fondly, "Father, I know very well you made certain about the fishing before you agreed to come out west, didn't you?"

Dr. Nuzum loaded the newcomers and their hand baggage into his sedan and drove them to the mid-town Barbara Hotel, their temporary quarters until Mrs. Sansum could locate a house to rent. She succeeded in finding a California-style redwood bungalow within easy walking distance of the Potter Clinic, at the south corner of Micheltorena and Castillo Streets.

Next day Dr. Nuzum introduced Dr. Sansum to the clinic staff. In his acknowledgements, Dr. Sansum reiterated the three objectives which Dr. Potter had formulated for his new clinic before leaving New York, which would be Dr. Sansum's guidelines in Santa Barbara. These objectives were:

First, the study of an unsolved group of more or less closely allied diseases of metabolism — diabetes, nephritis, high blood pressure, thyroid, gout, obesity and various nutritional disorders. This study was intended to be a concentrated effort to ascertain the fundamental causes of such diseases, better methods of treatment, and eventually, complete cures.

Second, to furnish a place where patients suffering from these diseases might receive careful, adequate examinations and the best treatment known to medical science, regardless of their finances.

Third, to afford a center for the specialized training of physicians, nurses, dietitians, and laboratory workers interested in this specialized field.

"Fortunately, the outlook for medical research is brighter than at any time in history," Dr. Sansum went on to say. "During the last few years, before and after the war in Europe, unusually large numbers of medical discoveries have been made. These have amply repaid all the time and money spent, and are fitting monuments to such men and women as the Knapps, the Billings, the Peabodys and other generous laymen who have given so unselfishly of their treasure to build and maintain hospitals and research laboratories."

It was on this occasion that Dr. Sansum first quoted to his audience the definition which he would repeat countless times in coming years:

"Medical research is the study of diseases of unknown cause, for which no satisfactory treatment is known."

Staff members and patients alike, still so fresh from their association with Dr. Potter, may have unknowingly put Dr. Sansum, the newcomer, on a sort of probation, waiting for him to prove himself. They need not have concerned themselves that Dr. Potter's successor would fail to measure up. If anything, Dr. Sansum's charismatic bedside personality proved more than equal to the "radium-like emanations" for which Dr. Potter was remembered.

Staff members in following weeks quickly overcame their reserve toward the new director and found themselves "putting out" beyond the call of duty, inspired by Dr. Sansum's example. Patients' faces invariably brightened when he entered their rooms on his cheerful morning rounds. They soon began calling him "Father Sansum."

"That affectionate nickname followed him for the rest of his life in Santa Barbara," recalls his long-time secretary, Elizabeth Buell. "It all began when Dr. Sansum started taking his diabetic children to a downtown theater for the Saturday vaudeville matinee. Whenever he approached the boxoffice with his 'family' in tow, the cashier would say to the doorman, 'Here comes Father Sansum!' — and the name stuck."

Since the Clinic was financially dependent upon support from the private sector rather than from any governmental subsidy, Dr. Sansum was obviously interested in checking over the Clinic's books. He found that total collections from patients and the laboratory during 1920 had amounted to $8,716, leaving an operating deficit of nearly $18,000. Deducting this figure from the Clinic's total resources of $40,000 left Dr. Sansum with a working balance of $22,000 to carry over into the new year.

The Clinic's securities reflected the current framework of history: mostly World War I Third and Fourth Liberty Loans, and the Victory Loan, having a par value of $26,900. Donations had ranged from $1.30 from "A Grateful Patient" to $3,750 from the Carnegie Corporation, and totaled approximately $13,000 for the year.

When hospital chairman George Owen Knapp formally introduced Dr. Sansum in his annual report for 1920, he added "The Potter Metabolic Clinic is working in close harmony with the other departments of the hospital. Splendid work is being done by the clinic in research work and the special care of patients suffering from diabetes and other metabolic diseases. Interesting and encouraging work is under way, and results of material value to mankind and the medical profession will, we believe, be forthcoming shortly."

The "interesting and encouraging work" launched by Dr. Sansum in his first year at the Potter Clinic — an extension of his program at Presbyterian Hospital under Dr. Woodyatt — was concentrated on developing a chemical compound which would duplicate in the laboratory test tube the pancreatic secretions which were missing or deficient in the metabolism of the diabetic patient.

Joining Dr. Sansum in this task was Dr. Norman R. Blatherwick, recently of Yale University, who was in charge of the laboratory. His paper on "Observations on Blood Fat in Diabetes" was the first of seventeen papers published by staff members during 1921.

Dr. Hilmar Koefod left the Clinic at this time to establish, in partnership with Dr. Rexwald Brown, the Santa Barbara Medical Clinic, which is still in existence.

Dr. Sansum published five learned papers during 1921, his first on the west coast, on such varied topics as "The preparation of sugar-free cream for diabetic patients," "Further studies on the nature of fever," "Dietetics at Cottage Hospital," "A simple method for the washing of bran for diabetic patients" (in collaboration with Florence H. Smith, the chief dietitian

30

whom he had brought with him from Chicago), and a resume entitled "The Potter Metabolic Clinic."

During Dr. Sansum's first full year as director, 174 patients were treated in the clinic, including 58 diabetics, 19 nephritics, 11 with hypertension, 19 for undernourishment, 18 with colitis and 13 cases of thyroid disease. At that time, the total bed capacity of Cottage Hospital was less than two hundred.

"We have welcomed all patients who came to us in need of these types of medical care," Dr. Sansum reported, "especially those without funds. During 1921 the clinic expended $6,335.27 for charity work."

In November Dr. Sansum moved his wife and son out of their rented bungalow to a newly-purchased house in a better location for his work, the northwest corner of Hollister Avenue (since renamed De la Vina Street) and Pueblo Street, only a block east of the clinic.

While Drs. Sansum and Blatherwick were pursuing their diabetes work in Santa Barbara, many other learned men around the globe were engaged in similar research. The first major breakthrough in the fight against diabetes came out of Canada late in 1921.

Dr. Frederick Banting, a young Canadian war veteran, had decided to devote himself to diabetes research rather than return to orthopedic surgery. His studies had convinced him that the pancreas produced a hormone that could metabolize sugar and relieve diabetic symptoms in experimental animals — so why not in man? At that time, such a radical theory was considered a "mirage" by the world's leading authorities.

Dr. Banting mapped out a plan for proving his theories, but he lacked laboratory facilities or animals with which to test his ideas. He approached various institutions of learning in Canada but was unanimously rejected and in some cases even ridiculed for his off-beat notions about diabetes. Finally, in the late spring of 1921, fate led Banting to Prof. J. R. R. Macleod, head of the Department of Physiology at the University of Toronto.

Macleod was impressed by young Banting's zeal, and somewhat by his ideas. Summer vacation was approaching; he could let Banting use an obscure storage room for a laboratory, and provide ten dogs for experimental purposes, all for a period of eight weeks. Macleod could also supply an assistant — his top medical student, 23-year-old Charles H. Best, who had just received his master's degree, to serve as Banting's chemist.

The teamwork accomplished by this pair was to elevate their names into the pantheon of such medical virtuosos as Hippocrates, Pasteur, Lister, Fleming and Salk.

With only two short months in which to establish their case before a critical and skeptical medical world, Banting and Best plunged into their task of extracting the as-yet unnamed hormone from the islands of Langerhans in dogs' pancreases. Scientists before them had failed to obtain potent secretions; Dr. Banting believed, and was proved correct in his belief, that this was because the pancreatic juices produced by the main body of the organ were destroying the mysterious sugar-burning hormone from the islands of Langerhans, during the actual extraction of the substance.

Since the islands of Langerhans are microscopic, they could not be dissected and the hormone obtained directly. To nullify the destructive action of the other pancreatic juices, Banting and Best launched their experiments by ligating the main pancreatic ducts in their dogs. After a few weeks the pancreases atrophied, leaving only the islands of Langerhans in a functional state.

32

The two young researchers made extracts of this degenerative tissue and tested it on dogs rendered diabetic by the surgical removal of their pancreases. In each case, a significant drop in blood sugar was noted.

"Our results on diabetic dogs were successful beyond our wildest hopes," Dr. Banting wrote in the February, 1922 issue of the *Canadian Journal of Laboratory and Clinical Medicine*. "Dogs almost at the point of death, emaciated and listless, when injected with this extract, recovered life and energy almost immediately. They gained weight and to all appearances were in perfect health, so long as they received daily injections of the extract. One test animal, which otherwise would have died within a few hours, was revived and restored to normal health for seventy days. We chloroformed it only to conserve our precious supply of the liquid."

Needless to say, Prof. Macleod extended indefinitely the period they could use the University's facilities.

Drs. Banting and Best, imbued with the feeling they were on the brink of a monumental discovery, ran another series of tests late in 1921 on laboratory rabbits, which proved one hundred percent successful. *But would the extract work on human diabetics?*

To test the safety factor, Banting and Best injected each other with the extract. There were no harmful side- or after-effects. The time had come to try the extract on a human diabetic.

In one of the most dramatic episodes in medical history, on the fateful morning of Wednesday, January 11, 1922, Banting and Macleod gave a subcutaneous injection of pancreatic extract to Leonard Thompson, an emaciated fourteen-year-old boy near death from diabetic acidosis, the next step to the usually fatal coma.

The waiting world of medicine learned the results of that injection in a report published by Dr. Banting in February:

*"The injection resulted in imme-
diate improvement. The excretion of
sugar became much less . . . The
acetone bodies disappeared from the
boy's urine. He became bright, more
active, looked better, and said he felt
stronger."* *

It was a medical discovery of such magnitude that
it led Dr. Banting to knighthood and a Nobel prize. The
news kindled first hopes in the hearts of millions of
doomed diabetics around the world.

Banting and Best were well aware of the epochal
importance of the miracle they had wrought. They both
realized that dishonest or incompetent persons could
manufacture the extract and defraud or endanger
diabetic patients. They wisely decided to patent the
substance, which they named "insulin" after the Latin
word *insula*, meaning island. The patent was then
assigned to a specially-created organization known as
the Insulin Committee of the University of Toronto,
who licensed drug manufacturers to make the substance
under rigid quality control. Because of this generosity
on the part of Banting and Best more than half a century
ago, diabetics today can obtain insulin anywhere in the
world, of standardized strength, and at low prices. Drs.
Banting and Best never profited one penny from the
fruits of their genius.

News of the discovery and successful testing of
insulin thrilled the entire world. Medicine hailed it as
the first diabetes breakthrough in a thousand years.
Diabetics — five hundred thousand of them in the
United States, according to the Metropolitan Life

---

* For the record, Leonard Thompson lived to be 27, dying in 1935 of
a malady unrelated to his diabetes, bronchial pneumonia. An
autopsy showed that the islands of Langerhans in Thompson's
pancreas were wholly atrophied.

Insurance Company, who heretofore had automatically rejected diabetics as bad insurance risks — began mobbing doctors' offices throughout the country, begging for insulin treatment. They were told that the life-saving extract was so far not available except in minute amounts in Toronto.

In Santa Barbara, Dr. Sansum received the news with great enthusiasm. After studying Dr. Banting's report thoroughly, he went to the laboratory where Dr. Blatherwick and his chief assistant, Dr. Marion Bell, were at work.

"In my judgement," Dr. Sansum said, "the Canadian reports offer a greater promise of success than our attempts [to compound a biochemical substitute for insulin]. Our clinic is admirably equipped to attack our problem from Banting's angle, don't you think?"

Dr. Blatherwick agreed. "What they can do in Canada, we should be able to duplicate in Santa Barbara. And improve on."

"I'm glad you feel that way," Dr. Sansum said enthusiastically. "I feel justified in ordering an entirely new line of work here. Using Banting and Best's techniques, we will attempt to manufacture our own insulin from animal glands."

4

Slaughterhouse
to Laboratory

The obvious first step toward any local production
of insulin had to be finding a dependable supply of fresh
canine pancreas glands. In view of the infinitesimal
amount of the life-saving hormone which was yielded
by a single animal, the municipal dog pound in a town
as small as Santa Barbara was not the answer. A clamor
of dissent from misguided anti-vivisectionists in the
community threatened another drawback.

The problem was still under investigation by Dr.
Sansum when a new development was announced by
the Toronto Group. Banting and Best reported success
in preparing a viable pancreatic principle from the
pancreases of fetal calves under five months development (a source which was impractical on a large scale
due to the cost) and from the normal pancreatic tissue of
adult oxen. Such extracts had been tested in dogs and
found to be both potent and non-toxic. Beef animals
were in abundant supply everywhere.

Drs. Walter Campbell and Almon Fletcher of the University of Toronto, under the direction of Banting and Best, injected these extracts subcutaneously to seven human diabetics suffering from advanced stages of the disease. Their results were summarized as follows:

"Following the production of what appears to be a concentrated, internal secretion of the pancreas and the demonstration of its physiological activity in animals, and under careful laboratory control, its relatively low toxicity, we are presenting a preliminary report on the pharmacological activity of this extract in human diabetes mellitus. Clinical observations at this juncture would appear to justify the following conclusions:

"(1) Blood sugar can be reduced to normal values.

"(2) Glycosuria (sugar in the urine) can be abolished.

"(3) The acetone bodies can be made to disappear from urine.

"(4) The respiratory quotient shows evidence of increased utilization of carbohydrates.

"(5) A definite improvement is observed in the general condition of these patients, and in addition the patients themselves report a subjective sense of well-being and increased vigor for a period following the administration of these preparations."

A major difficulty in extracting insulin from pancreatic tissue, Dr. Banting cautioned, was that trypsin, an enzyme which could produce autolysis (self-digestion), thereby destroying the insulin's potency on contact, was present side by side in the tissue. To obtain potent insulin, therefore, some method had to be devised to eliminate or counteract the trypsin. Forewarned, Dr. Sansum alerted his chemists to make every effort to nullify the trypsin enzymes before they could destroy the insulin.

Dr. Banting informed Dr. Sansum by transcontinental telephone that the Toronto Group was encountering extreme difficulty in extracting active insulin, and thus far had been unable to produce enough surplus to send any outside their own laboratory.

In Santa Barbara, the leading meat wholesaler was R. N. Gehl (pronounced gale), whose retail shop was situated in an historic landmark, the adobe San Carlos Hotel at 817 State Street. There, in 1846, Col. John C. Fremont had raised the American flag when he claimed Santa Barbara as a prize of war from Mexico.

Introducing himself to Gehl, Dr. Sansum explained his medical needs and asked whether Gehl shipped in his meat from Los Angeles, or whether he did his slaughtering in Santa Barbara. Gehl replied that he had a slaughterhouse on the west side of town, where Manitou Road joined West Pedregosa Street. Because of protests from neighbors and the city health officer, however, he was soon to move his malodorous stockpens and abattoir to Goleta, seven miles west.

When asked if Dr. Sansum could be allowed to purchase all the pancreases from beef animals slaughtered in the future, for use in diabetes research, Gehl was more than cooperative. He said there being little public demand for sweetbreads (pancreases), Dr. Sansum was welcome to them without charge.

When Gehl offered to have his slaughterhouse boss

toss the pancreases into a bucket and save them, Dr. Sansum hastily opted to be on hand when the animals were killed so he could pack the glands in ice immediately after they left the warm carcasses. Gehl was agreeable — but warned the doctor that Frank Lassett, his Italian-Basque slaughter man, always did his killing long before sunrise.

Thus it was, throughout this fateful month of April 1922, whenever Gehl's slaughter house foreman scheduled a beef killing in Manitou Ravine, Dr. Sansum set his alarm clock for 3 a.m. and was on hand at the killing floor with his portable ice chest, ready to refrigerate each warm pancreas while it was still steaming in the crisp predawn air.

A feverish anticipation such as he had not experienced since his first dissections at the Sprague Institute Laboratories as a freshman medical student seized Dr. Sansum the morning he turned over his first batch of beef pancreases to Dr. Blatherwick and his laboratory assistants in the Potter Metabolic Wing.

The laboratory technician who did most of the early work in extracting insulin for Dr. Blatherwick was Loyal C. Maxwell, a graduate of the University of Illinois and a former research chemist for the U.S. Bureau of Standards. For the benefit of readers with a technical bent, Dr. Maxwell has supplied this book with the following description of how insulin was extracted in the primitive stages of the art in 1922:

"As soon as the raw material was delivered from the slaughterhouse by Dr. Sansum," he wrote in 1977, "we immediately hashed it in an ordinary sausage grinder, extracting the insulin by vigorous stirring in cold seventy percent ethyl alcohol. Chilling and acidity were necessary to protect the precious insulin from destruction by the tryptic enzymes present in all pancreas tissue.

"The alcoholic extraction mixture was separated

from suspended solids by filtering and the clear filtrate was concentrated to the aqueous phase by low-temperature vacuum distillation. This concentrated solution was chilled again, and fatty material filtered out. The clear insulin-containing filtrate was brought to room temperature and the insulin precipitated by the addition of sodium chloride. The resulting insulin-salt cake was taken up in distilled water and the pH [measure of hydrogen concentration in grams per liter] adjusted to 2.5 with sulfuric acid. Alcohol and ether were used to precipitate the insulin after standing in a cold room, followed by still another alcohol wash and dissolving in redistilled water. The resulting essence was the substance we would inject in the diabetic patient."

Even after this complicated extraction process, the resultant insulin might not be active. The assay to establish potency prior to clinical use was performed by another technician, Melville Sahyun, who compared the local insulin with a standard sample supplied by Toronto University, using the blood sugar curve on fasted rabbits. Sahyun triumphantly reported that the first batch of Sansum-Blatherwick-Maxwell insulin exceeded in potency the Toronto master sample, leading to hopes that they had solved the trypsin self-digestion problem on their very first try. These hopes were dashed on the second batch, however, which proved to be inactive for reasons which could be ascertained only after tedious experimentation in the laboratory.

There were many other headaches in store, but that had been expected. By modern standards of purity, the pioneer 1922 insulin was crude and black as ink. The early yields did not average more than 500 units of insulin per pound of pancreatic material. (Within twenty years, Toronto had increased that yield to 900 units by improved methods.)

At the same time that Dr. Blatherwick and his team — Loyal C. Maxwell, Dr. Marion Bell, Melville Sahyun and Elsie Hill — were engaged in their early insulin work in Santa Barbara, similar work was going on at laboratories throughout the nation. Insulin manufacture was being attempted by such specialists as Dr. Frederick M. Allan of the Rockefeller Institute of Medical Research in Morristown, New Jersey; H. Rawle Geyelin of Columbia University Presbyterian Hospital in New York; Elliott P. Joslin of Boston; Russell M. Wilder of the Mayo Clinic in Rochester, Minnesota; J. R. Williams of Rochester New York; and Roland T. Woodyatt of Chicago, among others.

All were reporting severe problems of maintaining potent yields of extract, or no progress at all. The American press, sensing that a "race" was developing to see who could produce the first usable insulin in the United States, began covering the "competition" as a sporting event, to the amusement, if not the annoyance, of the medical research teams.

In April, disturbing news came out of Toronto, causing dismay in the ranks of U.S. research teams and consternation among diabetic patients when the news was leaked by a Toronto radio station: Banting and Best had "lost the method" of extracting insulin!

Details of the difficulty were never made public, but unofficial guesses were that Dr. Banting, after seeing insulin production well established in Toronto, allowed his assistant, Charles Best, to return to his medical school studies at the University, while Dr. J. B. Collip, a professor of biochemistry at the University of Alberta, took over Best's work in insulin production. Dr. Collip apparently was unable to obtain potent insulin and Best was recalled from school to start from scratch and recover the lost method.

Dr. Banting, in a personal letter to Dr. Sansum at that troubled time, made no attempt to cover up what was happening:

"Dear Dr. Sansum,

"We are publishing results as we get them and it is our desire to place whatever information is of value in this treatment before the profession as soon as possible, so that the investigation may be taken up and improved in other centers. We have not as yet a method of insulin preparation which we are sure enough of to publish. I may say that had it not been for an unforeseen hold-up in which we lost the method entirely, and had to commence all over, it would have been in print before now.

—Frederick Banting, M.D."

About this time, Santa Barbara's pioneer air pollution control advocates had managed to pressure Gehl into closing down his westside slaughterhouse and moving it out to Goleta. His stockyards were located on South Fairview Avenue at what is now the northeast corner of the municipal airport. This was seven miles away from Santa Barbara, transferring the malodorous nuisance well beyond range of sensitive nostrils in town, if not the olfactory organs of Goletans.

During the Goleta change-over period, Dr. Sansum was obliged to drive to Los Angeles once a week in a rented truck to bring back pancreatic tissue from hogs, sheep and steers. A large percentage of the materials proved inactive when tested on rabbits in Dr. Blatherwick's laboratory, leading Sansum to wonder if they may have been damaged by the action of the grain alcohol in which they had been transported from Los Angeles to Santa Barbara. This theory was later proved incorrect.

While Dr. Sansum and his associates were toiling in

the laboratory behind the scenes, the front office of the Potter Wing was being inundated with continuing inquiries from diabetics all over the United States, seeking reservations to come to Santa Barbara for insulin treatment.

While his colleagues in Toronto were struggling to recover their "lost method," Dr. Sansum had problems of his own — the reason for the spotty results from pancreatic tissue obtained from the Los Angeles abattoirs. Why were some batches active when tested on rabbits, and others sterile?

"We knew Dr. Sansum was giving a lot of heavy thought to that problem," an associate recalled many years later, "because of the frequency of his retiring to his private office where he began working on his famous 'Sansum sweaters' for friends and relatives. Knitting was his favorite diversion during times of extra-intense mental concentration."

As events were to prove, Dr. Sansum would need all the mental alertness he could muster to cope with a calamitous development in the near future.

5

Cowan and the Miracle of Insulin

When the experimental work on insulin was at its most critical stage at the Potter Metabolic Clinic, a distressing interruption threatened the entire project.

An essential part of Dr. Sansum's experimentation — as in medical laboratories everywhere — involved the use of dogs and rabbits for testing purposes. Throughout the United States in the early 1920s, anti-vivisection societies had sprouted like mushrooms. The goal of their sincere but misguided zeal was to make it a felony for scientists to experiment on living mice, rats, dogs, guinea pigs, rabbits or larger animals. Yellow journalists, with the Hearst newspapers in the vanguard, published reams of sensational and often fictional copy condemning animal experimentation as sadistic, unconstitutional, unnecessary, and un-American.

At the Potter Metabolic Clinic, as at similar laboratories throughout the world, the animal house was an indispensable adjunct to insulin research. Cruelty to these test animals was unheard of. All surgery was done under anesthetic and with sterile practices equal to those of any hospital operating room. Any work causing pain was handled with the same careful analgesic procedures as applied to human patients.

One of the part-time assistants engaged in animal work at the Potter Wing was a teacher from the State College located on the Riviera. He persuaded Dr. Blatherwick to permit him to take home a depancreatized dog for closer observation. Unfortunately the dog got loose and when he was picked up on the street by an ardent anti-vivisectionist, the incision in the animal's belly had become infected. In a few days, the experimental dog died.

Immediately a hue and cry went up in Santa Barbara. What was going on out there at Cottage Hospital? Rumors had it that white-coated sadists were torturing, blinding and crippling dogs and rabbits, all in the dubious name of science.

The guardian of the runaway dog was traced easily enough and the Santa Barbara chapter of the anti-vivisection society brought suit against the young laboratory worker, charging him with cruelty to animals. Superior Court Judge Samuel Crow presided over the jury trial which followed, with W. P. Butcher as defense attorney.

Pre-trial publicity brought hostile reaction against Dr. Sansum. A dog fancier all his life, Sansum's feelings were injured; and professionally, he realized that an adverse court decision in Santa Barbara could have judicial repercussions throughout the country, helping create a climate of public opinion which might conceivably make vivisection illegal. Such legislation could set back the cause of medical research a hundred years.

THE PARENTS OF DR. SANSUM, 1874
David Sansum and Elizabeth Frisby were from separate villages in England.
Emigrating to Wisconsin, they married in 1874 and raised a family of four boys and
four girls.

DR. SANSUM'S BIRTHPLACE IN WISCONSIN
was this farmhouse on the outskirts of Baraboo. Father David Sansum is standing near the well where the family milk supply was kept cool. The eight Sansum children

48

WILLIE SANSUM'S SCHOOL AND CHURCH

Above, the combination recreation center and community church in the suburb of Lyons on the edge of Baraboo, Wisconsin. His grade school, now an historic landmark, was the Lyons Common School five blocks from his home.

WILL SANSUM, QUARTERBACK
While attending Normal School at Stevens Point, young Sansum played football. This

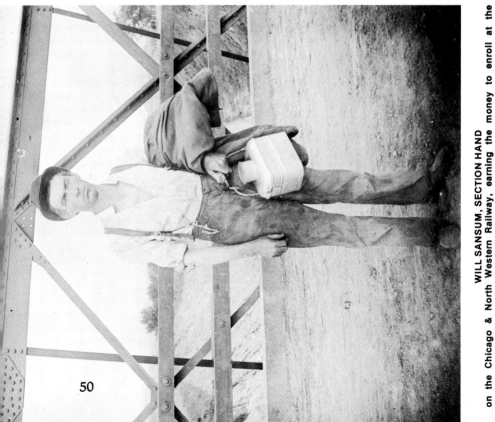

50

WILL SANSUM, SECTION HAND
on the Chicago & North Western Railway, earning the money to enroll at the

MABEL AND WILL SANSUM AS BRIDE AND GROOM, 1906

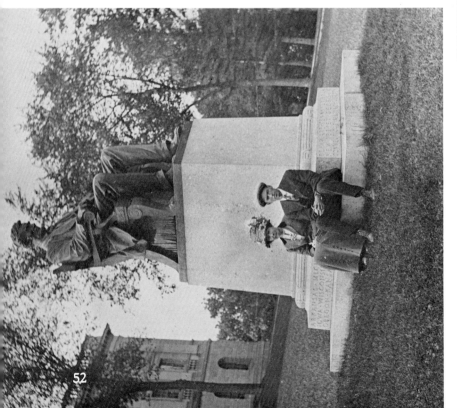

EARLY IN THEIR MARRIED LIFE
Will and Mabel Sansum posed for these pictures in Minneapolis, left, and in Madison. There are no known photographs taken of the future Dr. Sansum during his babyhood and adolescence.

52

Dr. William David Sansum was granted the degree of Doctor of Medicine Cum Laude by the Faculty of Rush Medical College, June 10, 1916, in recognition of the fact that he had completed the 6th or interne year complying with all of the conditions laid down by the Faculty and presenting a thesis entitled "Studies in Diabetes."

SHEEPSKIN AND GOWN

W. D. Sansum's hard-won diploma from Rush Medical College was a strip of vellum shown full size above. Below, the new doctor in his graduation gown. He was then thirty-six years of age.

THE SANSUM FAMILY AT A 1918 REUNION

Standing from left: Pearse, a butcher and chain store manager; Rose Martindale, Sauk County school teacher; William, the doctor; Roland, a railroad man; Margaret Engleking, a teacher; and John, future manager of Sansum Clinic. Seated, from left: Harriet Shults, a teacher; mother Elizabeth Frisby Sansum; father David Sansum; and Mary Fellows, a clerk and bookkeeper.

54

THE ORIGINAL POTTER WING
of the Santa Barbara Cottage Hospital, shown above, as it appeared in 1920 at the corner of Pueblo and Castillo Streets. Pioneer insulin patients were housed on the upper floor; the laboratory was on the ground floor. The picture below shows the Clinic reception room and admissions desk as of 1922.

55

DR. NATHANIEL BOWDITCH POTTER
who established the Potter Metabolic Clinic in New York City in 1916, moving it a year later to Santa Barbara.

SANTA BARBARA INSULIN PIONEERS

Upper left, Dr. Sansum as he appeared in 1920; upper right, his chief chemist, Norman Blatherwick Ph.D.; lower left, Melville Sahyun, who developed a method of standardizing insulin; lower right, Loyal C. Maxwell and Dr. Marion Bell, laboratory chemists.

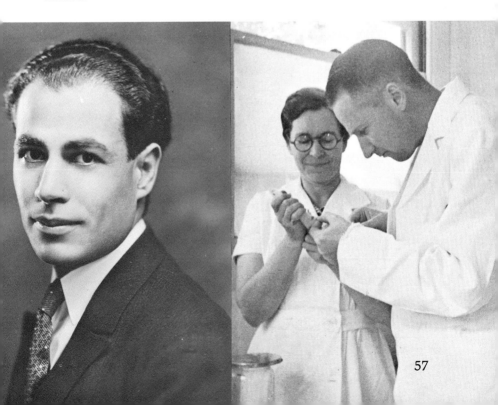

THE DISCOVERERS OF INSULIN
Clockwise from top left, Sir Frederick G. Banting, M.D.; Prof. Charles H. Best; Prof.
J.J.R. Macleod; and Prof. J.B. Collip, known as the "Toronto Group" in 1921.

DR. SANSUM'S FIRST INSULIN PATIENTS
gathered at Santa Barbara's Recreation Center in June 1924 for this group photo by Melville Sahyun, a clinic technician. [1] is Dr. Sansum; [2] Charles Cowan, the first patient ever to receive insulin made in the United States; [3] John Berger, a diabetic patient who did important laboratory work at the Potter Clinic; [4] Marion Fenner, a diabetic who was chief nurse at the Clinic, [5] Dr. Chapman; [6] Murray Vail; [7] Nancy Dickinson, daughter of a Hope Ranch philanthropist; [8] Margaret Hoffman, daughter of Bernhard Hoffman, "father" of Santa Barbara's Spanish look; and [9], Doris Fay Palmer, who endowed the Foundation with $50,000 a year out of gratitude for Dr. Sansum having saved her life in 1922.

59

8/1/22

BILL

M _Karl Klass_ No. 14479

ROOM

San Dimas Cal No. 7

SANTA BARBARA COTTAGE HOSPITAL

SANTA BARBARA, CALIF.

MAKE CHECKS PAYABLE TO THE SANTA BARBARA COTTAGE HOSPITAL

ROOM 7	DAYS FROM	
7/24/22 to 7/31/22 3		$ 21 00
OPERATING ROOM		
ANAESTHETIC	*PAID*	
MEDICAL SUPPLIES		
SURGICAL SUPPLIES	_Wright_	
NURSE'S BOARD		
EXTRA MEALS		
X RAY		
LABORATORY	_Routine_	5 00
PRESCRIPTIONS		26 00
	Cash 7/29/22	21 —
SEE NOTES AT BACK	_Bal._	5 00

PR	W ✓	MPR	MW	D	MIS.

HOSPITAL COSTS HAVE ESCALATED
since 1922 when Cottage Hospital billed diabetic patient Carl Klass $21 a week for a private room and meals at the Potter Clinic. Dr. Sansum provided insulin at no cost to patients since he considered it to be an "experimental drug" in 1922.

PROMINENT EARLY-DAY ASSOCIATES
of Dr. Sansum's were, upper left, George Owen Knapp, and upper right, Major Max C. Fleischmann, philanthropists who heavily endowed Cottage Hospital research efforts; lower left, Franklin R. Nuzum, M.D., chief of staff, and H. I. Burtness, M.D., as he appeared in 1929 as a Cottage Hospital internist specializing in diabetes.

61

EARLY-DAY CLINIC PERSONALITIES
included, top picture left to right, Barkley S. Wyckoff, D.M.D., oral surgery; Marion Fenner, R.N., chief nurse, and H. I. Burtness, M.D., diabetes specialist. The lower picture shows Dr. Sansum and members of his staff in one of their rare group assemblies.

THE DAY OF THE EARTHQUAKE
of June 29, 1925, saw Dr. Sansum's patients moved to the lawn near the Potter Clinic, as shown in this historic photograph by Mildred Root, R.N. Lower picture shows the home at the corner of West Pueblo Street and Hollister Avenue [now De la Vina Street] which the Sansums were occupying at the time of the earthquake.

63

MISS RUTH BOWDEN, B.S.
was Dr. Sansum's chief dietitian at the Potter Wing starting in 1924 and at Sansum Clinic until her retirement in 1958. She was also co-author of his several books on diet planning.

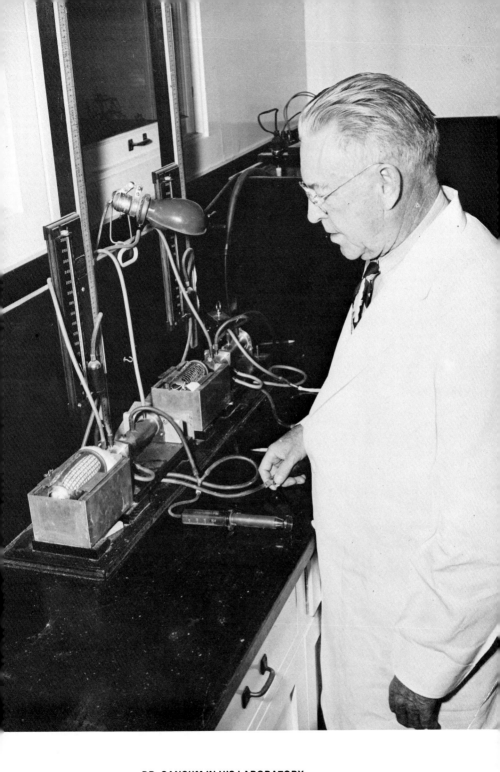

DR. SANSUM IN HIS LABORATORY
at Cottage Hospital, taking the blood pressure of a test rat. This was where he suffered his fatal seizure in January 1948.

THE SANSUM ESTATE IN 1935
The stately home and landscaped grounds are located at what is now the 2800 block of
Tallant Road, between the Samarkand Hotel and Oak Park, three blocks west of the

Dr. Sansum had given a loveable Boston terrier, Djin, to his son. The pet died after eating a weiner someone tossed up on the front lawn. An autopsy revealed that the pet had been poisoned with bichloride of mercury. There was no proof, but Dr. Sansum and his grieving family always believed that the anti-vivisectionists' hate campaign had triggered Djin's martyrdom.

When the case reached Judge Crow's courtroom, the defense called up two expert witnesses — Dr. W. D. Sansum and a local veterinarian, Dr. James H. Hester. Their combined testimony served to counteract the impassioned accusations of the plaintiffs, and the young laboratory worker was acquitted. Needless to say, a new regulation was strictly enforced at the Potter Clinic's animal house from then on — no laboratory animals could be removed from the premises under any circumstances!

Dr. Sansum, free to return to wrestling with the problem of why some batches of insulin were active and others impotent, came up with an idea to explore: was it possible that the activity of pancreatic extract might be related to how long before killing time the animals had been fed?

Blatherwick and Maxwell addressed themselves to that theory by feeding test rabbits one hour before slaughter. Without exception they obtained very potent extracts following this procedure. A rabbit's pancreas is exceedingly small, yet from this tiny amount of tissue the insulin content was as potent as that of the entire extract from two or three sheep!

One rabbit that was starved overnight gave an active extract; from two rabbits that were starved for forty-eight hours prior to killing, there was no activity. In some cases, Sansum and his laboratory colleagues prepared extracts from fed rabbits and tested them simultaneously with the starved rabbit extractions to assure that the techniques were exactly identical.

"I made a chart of all our alcoholic extracts which had been tested by the rabbit method," Dr. Sansum reported. "There were forty-two in all. Of these ten tested active. In seven instances the animals had been fed just prior to killing. Sheep were either taken from the rancher's wagon, or were taken from the feeding pens. Two of our calf extracts were made from calves that were killed as soon as they were taken from the rancher's wagon. One calf extract was made on a starved calf and was found to be inactive. In the other three cases of active extracts, we could not determine when the animals had been fed. One active beef extract, however, was secured from a beef that was taken directly from the pasture because they were short of meat at the butcher shop. All of the animals we obtained from the Los Angeles slaughterhouse had been starved for forty-eight hours previous to killing, a standard procedure which improved the meat for the consumer. The extracts made from fed rabbits, we found, had a different appearance from those made from starved animals; the extract is thicker."

Sensing that at long last he was on the right trail, Dr. Sansum arranged with Gehl to visit the holding pens out in Goleta where he was allowed to feed one steer a meal of rolled barley and corn sugar just previous to killing. The result was a definite increase in pancreatic activity.

"We appreciated this cooperation from Mr. Gehl," Sansum said later, "because the meat of animals fed just previous to slaughtering does not keep as well in the retail butchershop as does the meat of animals which have been starved before killing."

The active beef extracts from this experimentation resulted in obtaining a sufficient refrigerated supply of potent insulin to justify administering doses to a human being.

Even the method of administering insulin to a diabetic patient had been the subject of much experimentation by University of Toronto researchers. Several methods were explored by Banting and Best — oral, rectal, vaginal, intranasal, intravenous, and subcutaneous. They found that the most positive effects by far were obtained with subcutaneous injections. Intravenous injections were too short-lasting to be effective. Very weak or totally negative results came from the other methods.

Dr. Sansum and his associates in Santa Barbara were aware that the big moment had come: history was about to be made. What patient should receive the first injection of insulin made in the United States? At the moment, Dr. Sansum had thirty diabetes patients under his care in the Potter Wing. Seven were considered to be in the terminal stages of the disease, beyond hope of survival through diet therapy alone. Obviously, the few precious drops of American-made insulin available should go to the most desperate case.

In Dr. Sansum's view the options narrowed down to one obvious patient: Charles E. Cowan, the 51-year-old diabetic from Anaheim who had been given up as a hopeless case by his own doctor months before. As a last resort, Cowan had been admitted to the Potter Metabolic Clinic on the eighth of November, 1920 — at the same hour that Dr. Sansum was arriving in Santa Barbara with his family from Chicago.

Cowan had developed severe diabetes mellitus two years before, following a bad case of Spanish influenza, the disease which had killed thousands in 1918 in the worst epidemic in American history. A farmer, Cowan had his first inkling that something was seriously wrong with his health when he found that the gallon jug of drinking water he took with him to the orange groves every morning was consumed in less than two hours, still leaving him excessively thirsty.

At the Potter Clinic, Dr. Sansum had resorted to putting Cowan on a controlled diet which at times included as many as eighteen cakes of yeast per day in an attempt to burn out the excess sugar in his system. The day Cowan entered the clinic he weighed in at 112 pounds, an emaciated husk of a man five feet eight inches tall with a heavy frame. During the six months he had been hospitalized in Santa Barbara he had barely kept ahead of his acidosis on an 844-calorie diet, and was down to 95 pounds. His flesh resembled parchment taut-stretched over a skeleton. By all standards of evaluation, Charles Cowan was a terminal case.

"If insulin can prolong *this* man's life," Dr. Sansum said, "it can save anybody."

Wednesday, May 31, 1922, happened to be a day Cowan had not expected to see — his thirtieth wedding anniversary. It seemed an auspicious date on which to administer the first dose of insulin ever manufactured in the United States.*

Dr. Sansum's thumb was on the plunger of the syringe which shot three cubic centimeters of Santa Barbara insulin under Cowan's skin. Santa Barbara had "won the race," as the press had dubbed it, to produce the first insulin made inside the borders of the United States. But would it be successful on humans? Experimenters from coast to coast awaited the word from the Potter Metabolic Clinic as to Cowan's reaction to the insulin shot.

---

* Cowan was not the first patient in the United States to receive insulin. That distinction belonged to one James Haven, who was injected with *Canadian-made* insulin by his physician, Dr. John R. Williams, at the latter's office in Rochester, New York. In 1975, Dr. Charles Best of Toronto, co-discoverer of insulin, wrote Dr. Donald McMillan in Santa Barbara to report that Haven had received his insulin shot on May 21, 1922 — ten days earlier than Santa Barbara's Cowan.

Next morning the laboratory staff waited in breath-held suspense for the outcome of urine tests which would show whether Cowan was being desugarized. Bad news: the test tube showed ominous orange-red, evidence that sugar was still present in heavy amounts in Cowan's system. The same result showed in the test tube the second morning. We will let Cowan himself describe what happened on the third day:

Exactly thirty-five years later, in an interview with a reporter for the *Santa Ana Register* on the occasion of his 65th wedding anniversary, Charles Cowan, then in his eighty-ninth year, recalled:

"The third day after I received my first insulin shot, Dr. Sansum came racing down the hall to my room, forgetting his professional dignity in the excitement of bringing me a test tube that was *blue* — meaning I was sugar-free! Of course I didn't realize it at the time, but I was on the road to a complete recovery. Other diabetics in the Potter Wing shrieked with joy, realizing their own sentences of an early death had been reprieved. I was able to tell my beloved wife that I was no longer her 'sugar daddy' — I was her sugar-free sweetheart! And I have remained so to this day."

Dr. Sansum, with professional understatement, let the world know that his first insulin patient's response was "encouraging." Throughout the lay world, the news from Santa Barbara was greeted with rejoicing.

There were a host of difficulties to be solved in the administration of insulin to patients in the early days. Overdosing occurred frequently at first, which caused a patient's blood sugar to drop to dangerously low levels, bringing on the condition known as "insulin shock" which all diabetics have to guard against — sudden profuse perspiration followed in some cases by unconsciousness.

"I remember one such instance vividly," Dr. Franklin Nuzum related many years later. "John Berger, a patient who worked in Dr. Sansum's laboratory, was suffering from extreme malnutrition when he started taking insulin. On one occasion following a noon-day injection, Berger went to the beach in a streetcar. At mid-afternoon I met the streetcar conductor hurrying into the hospital foyer, carrying Berger over his shoulder like a sack of flour. Berger was wet with perspiration, and unconscious. Effective emergency treatment by Dr. Sansum and a nurse revived Berger, and he lived for forty-four more years. Insulin saved his life, as it saved the lives of countless thousands of other diabetics."

Dr. Sansum had enough insulin in the refrigerator to put another nineteen patients on the hormone in addition to Charles Cowan. In every case but one, the restoration to normal well-being and energy was as spectacular as it had been in Cowan's case.

To follow Cowan's clinical history to its conclusion: a year following his first injection of insulin, Cowan's weight had risen to 125 pounds. He was on a normal diet of 2,993 calories. By April of 1924 he weighed his normal 153 pounds, and his diet had stabilized at 2,417 calories. He was then released from the Potter Metabolic Clinic to return to tend his orange grove in Anaheim.

Charles E. Cowan was by far the most publicized of Dr. Sansum's thousands of successful diabetic cases. Cowan remained on insulin for the rest of the thirty-nine years of what he called "borrowed time," returning to Santa Barbara periodically for routine checkups. For many years Cowan's dosage remained steady at forty units of U-80 NPH insulin daily before breakfast, and an occasional five units of regular insulin if the need arose. In later life, Cowan did not develop the ailments suffered by some elderly diabetics, such as retinal disease, kidney failure, or gangrene of the feet. His blood pressure was steady at a healthy 142/80, and he retained his alert mental faculties.

Cowan outlived Dr. Sansum by a full decade. He was ninety when he died at Anaheim on February 10, 1958. The coroner's autopsy indicated that Cowan's death was due to the normal aging process, not to diabetes mellitus.

6

Trouble with
Prohibition Agents

Nation-wide press reports that the new insulin treatment for diabetes was now a *fait accompli* in Santa Barbara brought a renewed influx of applicants seeking admission to the Potter Clinic. Dr. Sansum regretfully turned away all such applicants where insulin, rather than diet therapy was indicated, saying that his production of the miracle extract was still so limited that such supplies as he did manufacture had to be reserved strictly for terminally ill patients for whom insulin was a last resort. (Of these, he only lost one case, a child whose parents inexplicably discontinued the insulin.)

Encouraging news had come out of Canada, however. The Toronto Group had assigned rights to the Indianapolis pharmaceutical house of Eli Lilly & Company to mass produce insulin under their brand name of Iletin. The Lilly Laboratories informed Dr. Sansum that they were having extraction problems, so there was no way to predict when Iletin would begin reaching physicians across the country.

Not to be overlooked in the general euphoria attending Charles Cowan's spectacular recuperation under insulin treatment was Case No. 3 of the historic "first twenty" patients put on insulin that summer of 1922. He was Carl Klass, a bright, emaciated boy of eleven from San Dimas, who was in the penultimate stages of diabetic acidosis when he checked into the Potter Clinic.

Fifty-five years later, Klass described his experiences as Dr. Sansum's first case of juvenile-onset diabetes, a disease which differed in some respects from adult diabetes:

"I was literally at death's door when I arrived in Santa Barbara. The morning that Mr. Cowan and eighteen other diabetes patients lined up for their insulin shots, with me as the latest arrival being at the end of the line, the other patients took one look at my skin-and-bones condition and insisted I go ahead of them. After my first shot I began to blossom, even more sensationally than had Mr. Cowan, for I became completely sugar-free within twenty-four hours. Almost immediately Dr. Sansum put me on a normal diet. It was like being born again!"

In a letter to Carl's anxious parents in San Dimas, Dr. Sansum wrote, "Your boy is gaining weight at the rate of half a pound per day. From the living skeleton we admitted to the hospital, he now appears like a normal, happy, active child of his age. By the older methods practiced here prior to the discovery of insulin, Carl would have had a life expectancy of from one to six months, no more. We now feel that he is on his way to leading a normal, vigorous life."

Dr. Sansum's prediction proved correct. Mr. Klass, paying a nostalgic visit to the Sansum Medical Research Foundation in 1976 fifty-four years after his first insulin shot, made this report:

"The Potter Clinic was like a happy home to us diabetic patients. Everyone called the doctor 'Father Sansum'. He would make his rounds at ten o'clock every morning, jolly and beaming. One morning I got shaky. I had gone into the bathroom and locked myself in a booth, where I passed out from insulin shock. The nurses were about to break down the door to get me, when Father Sansum arrived. He took one look at the twelve-inch opening below the door, and somehow managed to crawl inside the booth, unlock the door and carry me out. He forced orange juice down me, a standard procedure in those days to cure the 'shakes', as we called it. Orange juice was not ordinarily included in the high fat, low carbohydrates they fed diabetics at that early date.

"I remained in the Cottage Hospital for three years. The charges for my treatment were $21 a week, including the insulin. I remember one morning around two o'clock, my roommate, the famous Mr. Cowan, and I were awakened by a noise outside. We went to the window of our upper-story room in the Potter Wing and looked out. Below us was Father Sansum, just back from Los Angeles with a load of milk cans filled with raw pancreas glands he had picked up at a slaughterhouse. It must have been three a.m. before he got to bed, but at ten o'clock next morning he was making his rounds, as jolly as could be. Few people knew how terribly hard Father Sansum worked for us.

"He took a deep personal interest in every patient under his care. To illustrate: I had improved so rapidly under insulin that I was allowed to wander around the town. I liked to go down to the harbor and rent a rowboat every chance I got. Dr. Sansum had ordered us never, under any circumstances whatever, to eat anything outside the hospital, since diet control was so vital to the success of his treatment. But one day after some strenuous boating at the harbor, I was so hungry I bought a hamburger. Next morning Father Sansum came to my bedside and asked accusingly, 'What did you eat at the beach yesterday?'

" 'How did you know?' I asked in astonishment. 'Whatever it was,' he retorted, 'turned up in your urine sugar test.' When I confessed what I had done, he appeared to be terribly hurt. I felt guilty for months afterward. Father Sansum would not tolerate any of his patients going off their regimen. In fact he was known to dismiss patients who violated his rules."*

---

* On August 28, 1972, at the age of 61, Carl Klass, then running an electrical appliance store in Laguna Beach, returned to Santa

After treating his first twenty patients with insulin for one month, Dr. Sansum sent a detailed report to Prof. Macleod in Toronto, describing the laboratories at his command and ending with a medical SOS:

"Here in Santa Barbara we are in urgent need of assistance in some of our near-fatal cases, and our experience in the manufacture of pancreatic extract is too limited to warrant our hoping to get into mass production in time to save their lives."

Reflecting the true spirit of cooperation which is the hallmark of sincere men of science everywhere, Prof. Macleod responded at once by releasing to Dr. Sansum, in advance of publication, Toronto's latest findings in the technical production of insulin from animal glands, thus giving Dr. Blatherwick and his associates the advantage of more than a year's experiment work by their Canadian colleagues.

As Dr. Sansum continued his predawn visits to the slaughterhouse to obtain fresh source material for insulin extraction, the clinic's business office came up with some disturbing figures. By their computation of the cost of manufacturing insulin, the price per patient per day was $100, mostly due to assay costs requiring the maintenance and care of an animal colony, in addition to labor and overhead. When, hospital superintendent G. W. Curtis asked Dr. Sansum, could they begin billing patients for insulin?

"Never — so long as it is classified as an experimental drug," Dr. Sansum replied. "Later on, perhaps. But not as yet."

Barbara where he was presented with a bronze medal from the Joslin Diabetes Foundation Inc. of Boston, "for having lived 50 courageous years with diabetes without complications." At that time Klass estimated that he had given himself more than 51,000 insulin injections, over 35,000 of them in the abdomen.

During the next few weeks, Dr. Sansum paid over $1,400 out of his own pocket to provide free insulin for his patients.

He kept only the most severe diabetic cases in the hospital. Less ill patients could continue treatment at home, but it was necessary for them to be thoroughly schooled in the technique of insulin injections, sterilization of equipment, and, equally important, how to measure out exact portions of their food, gram by gram, and how to exchange foods of equal caloric value to best suit their individual tastes.

"Because of his early training and natural ability, Dr. Sansum was fundamentally a teacher," reported a colleague, Alfred E. Koehler, M.D. "He was a pioneer in the work of health education for patients. He advocated the theory of prevention of illness by conducting classes to teach patients the fundamental principles of good health — a theory which was preached for many years by Dr. Sansum before it was generally accepted in the profession. Starting in 1922, he organized classes for his diabetic patients, later extending his lecture courses for all the hospital patients. In the beginning these courses were limited to nutrition, but later they were enlarged to include many medical subjects of interest to the patient."

News of the sensational developments in diabetes therapy out in Santa Barbara reached the ears of Dr. Henry S. Pritchett, the president of the Carnegie Corporation in New York. In midsummer 1922 that distinguished gentleman paid a surprise personal visit to Santa Barbara to observe things for himself, not only as a director of the Potter Clinic, but in his capacity as chief of the Carnegie Corporation.

"Our results have been quite satisfactory," Dr. Sansum understated himself to Dr. Pritchett, "but we simply must devise cheaper ways of producing insulin. A study of the intricate chemistry of the hormone will undoubtedly add materially to our knowledge of the oxidative processes going on in the body about which practically nothing is known at present. But the great gains seem to be that diabetic patients under insulin will not only be sugar-free, but will be able to resume normal diets along with the strength and well-being which can come only from the use of balanced food."

Dr. Pritchett observed that new machinery was being installed in a portion of the hospital's morgue — the only space available — including copper distillation stills, a larger press, and more efficient apparatus for handling the many filtering and dehydrating procedures. (A laboratory assistant was working with ether in this room a few months later, foolishly smoking a cigar, igniting the fumes and causing an explosion which hospitalized him for weeks.)

Before leaving Santa Barbara, Dr. Pritchett told Dr. Sansum that the Carnegie Corporation's annual meeting was coming up around the first of October and suggested that it might be advantageous for his cause if he prepared a summary of his accomplishments in the preparation and administration of insulin in Santa Barbara and sent it to the board of directors, as Dr. Banting and his Toronto Group would be doing, since they also received Carnegie funding.

That same evening, Sansum dictated such a report and gave it to Dr. Pritchett to personally take back to New York. Sorely in need of a rest and change of scenery, Dr. Sansum took two weeks off, ostensibly to go fishing in the Sierra Nevada. Instead he impulsively boarded a train for Toronto, where he met with the celebrated "Group" — Banting, Best, Collip and Macleod. The Canadians received their distinguished colleague from California with great cordiality and favored Dr. Sansum with an intensive private seminar regarding their insulin work.

While Dr. Sansum was away, the Carnegie

Corporation convened its annual executive meeting in Manhattan. The presiding officer, Dr. Pritchett, reported on his visit to Santa Barbara and read Dr. Sansum's report regarding work in progress at the Potter Metabolic Clinic, a report which frankly admitted their difficulties in extracting the product.

"Dr. Sansum's brilliant success," Dr. Pritchett told the Carnegie executives, "and the still more brilliant prospects for the future which it holds out, holds great encouragement for us all. As you all know, Mr. Carnegie has always in mind the desire to 'find the efficient man and let him do his work'. This Corporation has always believed that its financial support will advance the cause of medical knowledge and thereby increase human happiness and usefulness in the most desirable fashion. Not every research endeavor, of course, can show the spectacular results which have come out of Dr. Sansum's investigation; but patience and long-continued study adds, little by little, to man's store of knowledge, enriches life, and helps to turn away misfortune.

"Not the least pleasing feature of this ongoing investigation," Dr. Pritchett went on, "lies in the generous and admirable attitude in which two sets of investigators — in Toronto and in Santa Barbara — each of whom has received modest help from the Carnegie Corporation — have cooperated toward their common goal. It was a graceful and generous act on the part of Dr. Macleod and his colleagues to put at the service of Dr. Sansum the full results of their important researches, but this action is in entire consonance with the spirit and the purpose of true science."

The Carnegie executives were so impressed that they voted a cash gift of $15,000 to Santa Barbara, funds which Dr. Sansum promptly set to use by adding staff members to work in Dr. Blatherwick's laboratory in the Potter Wing.

A press release of the Carnegie Corporation meeting was published on the front page of the New York *Times* on Sunday, October 8, 1922. This publicity, picked up by newspapers all over the world, gave renewed hope and assurance to diabetics everywhere.

SERUM PROVES BOON IN FIGHTING DIABETES proclaimed the *Times'* headline on page one.* The subheads read "Ravages of disease checked by insulin./Treatment developed with rare success in Santa Barbara clinic./Relief almost certain./Carnegie Corporation aids research."

The after-effects of the *Times* publicity were incredible, opening the gates for the greatest stampede of healthseekers to Santa Barbara that the city had yet experienced. *Free* insulin in Santa Barbara? The only place outside of Canada where insulin was available at any price?

Men, women and children in the last stages of diabetes mellitus began queuing up at the clinic's admissions desk, begging to be admitted for preparatory diet therapy, if nothing else, while they waited their turn for the precious lifegiving insulin. As before, Dr. Sansum was obliged to accept only cases where fatal coma seemed imminent, until his supply of insulin picked up. Milder cases were advised to wait, since the Eli Lilly supply of Iletin was expected momentarily.

Largely due to the New York *Times* story, the Potter Wing's limited bed space was overnight booked to capacity. Fortunately, during past months a benefactress, Mrs. Anna Blakesly Bliss of Casa Dorinda in Montecito, had donated a new children's wing to Cottage Hospital, facing the corner of Bath and Pueblo Streets. The Bliss Wing made it possible for the hospital to turn over its entire main floor of the central building

---

* The New York *Times*, usually impeccably accurate in its choice of words, erred in calling insulin a serum; it is actually an extract.

to handle Dr. Sansum's unexpected influx of diabetics. To meet the need for insulin, the Potter laboratory was now able to produce enough to handle the seriously ill cases, but it meant that Blatherwick, Maxwell, Sansum and associates had to work nights and Sundays for a considerable period.

"It is a soul-wrenching thing," Dr. Sansum told a reporter, "to have to turn away a desperately sick person when you know you hold the key to his recovery, but don't have enough keys to offer."

Dr. Sansum realized he could no longer rely on the Goleta slaughterhouse for enough raw material to manufacture insulin in the amounts needed to handle the increasing demand. Until such time as Eli Lilly & Company could get tooled up for large-scale production, he would have to go to Los Angeles slaughterhouses for his raw material.

The two-hundred-mile round trip from the Hauser Packing Company abattoir in Los Angeles necessitated the procurement of large amounts of grain alcohol to preserve the fresh glandular material en route from packing house to laboratory. But this was 1922, when Prohibition was the law of the land. Alcohol, even for the most valid of scientific uses, was hard to come by.

Law enforcement under the Eighteenth Amendment was erratic and often arbitrary. Bootlegging and rum-running were rife in Santa Barbara County, which has the longest coastline of any county in the United States, offering scores of secluded coves and beaches where the booze merchants could land their illicit cargoes. Yet Dr. Sansum was to learn from his own bitter experience that not even a physician engaged in saving the lives of his fellow men rated any respect from over-zealous "revenuers."

Late one winter night, just as the first pink streaks of dawn were staining the horizon, Dr. Sansum was northbound along the Coast Highway, returning from

Hauser's slaughterhouse to Santa Barbara. The back of his big Dodge Brothers sedan was loaded with tin milk cans filled with bovine pancreases pickled in alcohol.

Near Malibu a motorcycle officer thumbed him to the side of the road. He was a "Prohi" on beach patrol. "What's in the milk cans — milk or booze?" demanded the officer.

"Animal glands," Dr. Sansum answered. "We take them to a hospital in Santa Barbara and squeeze out the insulin."

"Insulin? What's insulin?"

"If you should ever contract diabetes, God forbid, insulin would save your life, officer."

The revenue agent probed Sansum's cargo with his flashlight beam. "Open up a can so I can have a look," he ordered.

Sansum shrugged wearily and complied. The officer sniffed the contents of the open milk can and recoiled from the odor.

"That's alcohol! You can't transport alcohol!"

"But this is for scientific purposes —"

"I don't give a damn what it's for, I'm giving you a ticket for violating the Prohibition laws. You can do your explaining to a federal judge. What's your name and where's your driver's license?"

Any infringement of the Eighteenth Amendment was a serious matter in 1922. If a hostile judge levied a fine or even a jail sentence, it could shut down the Potter Clinic's insulin manufacturing program.

Sorely depressed, Dr. Sansum suffered the indignity of having his load of pancreases impounded by the law. The next evening in Santa Barbara, he unwrapped a copy of the *Chicago Daily News* which he received by mail and began reading about what was happening in his former home town. He suddenly startled his wife and sister-in-law by lowering the paper and giving a shout of pure joy.

"I think I've found the solution to our problem of obtaining alcohol for our laboratory work!" he cried. "Listen to this news item, out of Toronto: 'Miss Elizabeth Hughes, fifteen-year-old daughter of the American Secretary of State Charles Evans Hughes, has seemingly been cured of severe diabetes and has returned to her parental home in Washington D.C. after undergoing treatment here for the past five months under the personal care of Dr. Frederick G. Banting of the University of Toronto.' Isn't that wonderful?"

Mabel Sansum and her sister exchanged puzzled glances. "What has that got to do with alcohol?" Mabel asked. "I don't quite understand —"

"Don't you see, mother? If a man as important and powerful as our Secretary of State has a diabetic child, and I tell him how I face a fine and possible jail sentence for transporting alcohol for the purpose of extracting insulin, don't you think he'll do something in my behalf?"

Dr. Sansum dashed off a long letter to Secretary Hughes. Within the hour of its arrival in Washington, Hughes was on the telephone with the Secretary of the Treasury, whose department had the responsibility of enforcing the Prohibition laws.

Hughes' political muscle got instant results. Dr. Sansum received a telegram signed by the Secretary of State of the United States, telling him that the Treasury Department had granted permision for him to purchase and transport as much alcohol as he might require for his insulin work, and that the charges pending against him in Los Angeles had been dropped.

The following morning when Drs. Sansum and Blatherwick presented themselves at the Federal Building in Los Angeles to pick up their alcohol permit, they found a figurative red carpet spread for them.

"The Prohibition authorities were much impressed with so generous and unusual an offer coming from high in the federal government," Dr. Sansum wrote the parents of one of his juvenile patients. "When we went to their office they treated us more like high government officials than like ordinary nobodies as they had done on previous occasions."

Now that they possessed federal licenses to procure and transport alcohol in any amount, it was possible for Blatherwick and Sansum to arrange for an extraction plant at the slaughterhouse in Los Angeles, thereby eliminating the night runs from Santa Barbara. But the first three weeks after putting the new plant into operation resulted in the worst slump in insulin manufacture that Sansum had yet experienced.

On analyzing the inferior batches, Dr. Sansum found peptones and proteoses indicating considerable enzyme digestion in the raw pancreatic material. On investigation, he found that the workmen in the Los Angeles packing house had been grossly negligent in handling the glandular tissue. In some cases, six hours had elapsed before the glands were moved from the killing floor to the freezing room.

"We corrected that situation in a hurry," Dr. Sansum reported later. "We had one man trimming the glands of fat and connective tissue right on the slaughtering floor, and placing them immediately on cracked ice. We have two men working in a nice clean extraction room adjoining the slaughterhouse laundry. We have equipped this room with a 28-ton screw press and mixing machine for stirring the glandular material after it has been mixed with alcohol. This mixer is power-driven."

Another advantage of the new arrangement was that Dr. Sansum could ship his alcohol and other accessories by highway express, which returned the filtered extract to Santa Barbara in ten-gallon cans. They also called for and picked up the empties at Cottage Hospital, taking them to the packing plant a hundred miles away, and returned the filled cans on a regular schedule.

Since large quantities of alcohol were needed in the extraction process of insulin, Dr. Sansum's source of supply was a wholesale distillery in San Francisco. An oaken barrel of alcohol was extremely heavy. To ship it by railway or private truck would have been prohibitively expensive, so Dr. Sansum resorted to the slow, but relatively cheap coastal steamships which in the early Twenties still made Santa Barbara a port of call.

"Not one barrel of alcohol was ever unloaded at Stearns Wharf without it having been tapped on the way down from 'Frisco," Dr. Sansum reported ruefully. "Some portion, a gallon or so, had always been withdrawn for private consumption by a person or persons unknown."

Having overcome the obstacle of alcohol procurement, with its promise of an unlimited ongoing supply of quality-controlled insulin, Dr. Sansum now decided the time had come to approve the unrestricted admission of diabetic patients to the full capacity of Cottage Hospital, presaging a new era which came to be known as "the insulin years."

7

A Dramatic New Diet Discovery

Early in 1923 the Eli Lilly Research Laboratories in Indianapolis informed Dr. Sansum that their commercial insulin, Iletin, would shortly be in mass production and ready for world-wide distribution. It was gratifying to the Santa Barbara group to learn that many of the techniques employed by Lilly matched those developed in the laboratory by Sansum and Blatherwick.

Lilly promised to hold costs to five cents a unit (a "unit" meant the measure of the sugar-burning strength of one gram of insulin), to come in five cubic centimeter ampoules in two different strengths, five or ten units per cubic centimeter. This translated to a cost of from $1.25 to $2.50 per teaspoonful.

A diabetes patient with a typical daily dosage of forty units could thus obtain the life-supporting drug for two dollars a day, as contrasted to the $100 per day it was costing Sansum to manufacture insulin in Santa Barbara in the early period — ample proof of the efficacy of American mass production.

Eli Lilly & Company made their first shipment of experimental Iletin in February 1923, to ten selected doctors in the United States (Dr. Sansum being one of the ten), but in such small amounts that it became obvious that local production of insulin would have to continue, otherwise desperately-ill patients would have to be turned away.

However, even the limited amounts of Iletin which Lilly was furnishing free for experimental purposes made it possible for Dr. Sansum to instruct certain patients on how to inject themselves with the drug, so that he could send them home with a syringe and a month's supply of Iletin, thus freeing precious bed space for new patients.

Faced with the continuing need to manufacture insulin in quantity, Sansum and Blatherwick began expanding their facilities by installing the proper machinery. In the early phases of their work they had had to make as many as five pressings by hand; the addition of a crude grape press still required up to three pressings to extract all the active material.

At this juncture Dr. Sansum was materially assisted in modernizing his insulin manufacturing facility by a wealthy furniture dealer from Louisville, Kentucky, E. F. Palmer, whose daughter, Doris Fay, was one of the first diabetic patients to be admitted to Potter Clinic for treatment. Palmer, who later retired to Santa Barbara to live, became so interested in the manufacture of insulin that whenever he could spare time from his business he would come to Santa Barbara and volunteer his services around the clinic. Dr. Sansum set him to work grinding animal glands, the first step in insulin manufacture. Noting how crude and inefficient the grape press was, Palmer donated a hundred-ton hydraulic press to the clinic, which made it possible to squeeze out all the insulin extract in one press.

The new extraction room was equipped with three steam-heated water baths holding large flasks. The temperature could be controlled precisely and automatically with a patented Fulton sylphon regulator. The room was further equipped with two electric stoves for the manufacture of absolute alcohol and the recovery of ether.

In his new class for patients, Dr. Sansum emphasized that at the present state of the art, insulin had to be injected under the skin with hypodermic needles, since experimentation had proved that unsatisfactory results were obtained with desugarization if the insulin was taken intravenously, or by nasal, rectal, vaginal or oral administration.

This created problems with some patients, especially children, who were squeamish about puncturing themselves with a needle. In a time before disposable plastic syringes for one-time use came on the market, the patient also had to learn how to sterilize needles with or without an autoclave; how to insert the needle without puncturing a blood vessel; and how to be positive that no air bubble was present in the needle which could cause a fatal embolism if it entered the bloodstream.

Recognizing this problem, Dr. Sansum told his staff that the laboratory's number one priority had to be to perfect a capsule or tablet so that insulin could be taken like aspirin, by mouth. Many years and $150,000 later, Dr. Sansum had to abandon this idea; gastric juices in the stomach, mainly hydrochloric acid, had the property of instantly destroying insulin pills' effectiveness.

Sansum signed a contract guaranteeing him the entire output of animal pancreases from the Hauser plant in Los Angeles, and by improved methods of extraction, was able to reduce the daily cost of insulin per patient from $100 to under $20 before the year ran its course.

When Lilly's commercial insulin finally hit the market, it enabled the Potter Metabolic Clinic to announce that as of March 1, 1923, it would no longer supply free insulin to patients (this did not apply to needy patients, since it was a fundamental tenet of Dr. Sansum's that no one would ever be turned away for lack of money to pay for treatment).

"Henceforth we will charge for our own experimental insulin at the rate of three cents per gram of sugar utilization or burning power," Dr. Sansum announced. "At present this is less than our actual cost, since it is not including the cost of new equipment and its depreciation. Our annual budget is a generous $40,000, but our expenses are running $60,000 annually. We must therefore charge our patients for insulin or go bankrupt. All of the money collected on sales of our insulin, however, will be set aside exclusively for insulin research."

In the laboratory, Dr. Blatherwick and his assistants were embarking on a new by-path, other than their main objective of developing oral insulin. They were manufacturing glucokinin, an anti-enzyme made from grass which, when mixed with powdered insulin and administered to rabbits, protected the insulin from being consumed by digestive juices. This line of experimentation, however, was to end in failure when applied to humans.

Reflecting the tremendous demand for insulin, the Potter Metabolic Clinic was now budgeting $2,000 per month for Iletin. By midsummer, Sansum and Blatherwick succeeded in producing insulin with an unprecedented sugar-burning power of 35 to 40 grams per cubic centimeter. Dr. Sansum, in a letter to one of his patients, wrote "I am pleased to inform you that our own product is less irritating than the Lilly product. We are now far enough ahead of the game that we can set aside a month's supply for each patient on our roster.

We are getting some remarkable results, in young patients especially, and with those who have had a severe grade of diabetes for only a short time before coming to us."

By the end of 1923 Dr. Sansum's insulin production had progressed to the point where he could, for the first time, report to the Cottage Hospital board, "We now have an unlimited supply of insulin. The cost of manufacturing has been drastically reduced but it is still a comparatively expensive drug, and cheaper methods of production must, and can be found. We have every reason to believe that a substantial reduction in price can be brought about during the coming year. We are also striving to obtain better quality insulin."

So far, no scientist in the world knew the exact chemical composition of insulin, although researchers throughout the country, comparing notes at regular intervals, were encouraged by the accumulating evidence that the hormone was a simpler compound than they had originally supposed.*

In the spring of 1924 California was hit by a disastrous outbreak of hoof-and-mouth disease among cloven-hoofed animals. Throughout the state, herds of cattle, sheep and hogs afflicted with the highly-contagious disease were slaughtered and the carcasses destroyed in mass cremations. All persons entering or leaving any affected county by public or private transport, including school buses and railroad trains, were required to step onto pads saturated with creosote-based antiseptic before boarding, which

---

* The answer to this fundamental question — the chemical makeup of insulin — was to remain a mystery for another thirty years. In 1953, Frederick Sanger succeeded in isolating insulin in a pure crystalline form, and established that it was a protein composed of a chain of fifty-one amino acids. The first synthesization of insulin occurred in China in 1966.

brought the acrid reek of sheep dip to California homes, business houses and public buildings during the run of the epidemic.

The effects of hoof-and-mouth disease in closing down slaughter houses were catastrophic, curtailing all experimental work on insulin, including Dr. Sansum's operations.

Eventually the quarantine was lifted and the Hauser packery reopened its killing floor, assuring the Potter Clinic of a continuing supply of raw material for insulin making.

During Dr. Sansum's fourth year at the clinic his laboratory was able to purify insulin to such a degree that ten grains, or two-thirds of a gram of the desiccated product, were sufficient to maintain even a critically-ill patient for one year. Work continued, albeit unsuccessfully, to develop an insulin product that could be ingested by mouth.

"If oral insulin can be perfected for human use," Dr. Sansum said in his annual report for 1924, "its clinical importance will be second only to the discovery of insulin itself!"

The volume of research projects now in progress taxed the cramped quarters of the Potter Wing. To meet the need for more space, the ground floor under the maternity wing of the hospital, formerly used for help's quarters and a nurses' classroom, was converted into five laboratories for the use of Sansum and Blatherwick and their staff.

During 1924 the patient volume doubled to just under 500 patients, only 151 of whom were diabetic — reflecting dramatically how the national availability of Iletin was relieving Santa Barbara from being the only source of insulin treatment in California.

Although the diabetes outlook had brightened, the scourge was still far from conquered, as evidenced by the fact that in the United States the death rate from diabetes had not materially lowered since the discovery of insulin three years before.

This disturbed Dr. Sansum deeply. It stuck in his mind at home and in the laboratory; it even tormented his dreams at night. How could the death rate from diabetes be reduced?

An integral part of Dr. Sansum's treatment of diabetic patients was controlled diet in conjunction with insulin therapy. Could it be that the long-accepted high fat starvation diets had something to do with diabetes mortality? Was it more difficult for a diabetic person to utilize fat than it was for him to utilize starch and sugar? If so, this was diametrically opposite traditional dietetic practices, contradicting long-established and un-challenged teachings by authorities. Dr. Sansum recalled that many of his patients had gained weight and strength on high-fat diets, but had lacked energy, ambition and the feeling and appearance of general good health. Something was wrong; a key part of the puzzle was missing. He recalled one patient in particular, a wealthy businessman from Denver, who had come to the Clinic for treatment of diabetes. After returning to Colorado, he reported that he had gained weight but did not have enough stamina to carry on his ordinary daily affairs. Dr. Sansum pondered his case, and began to ask himself: was diet responsible for the lack of energy?

An article had come to his attention in a German-language medical journal, written by Drs. D. Aldersberg and O. Porges, a diabetes research team at the University of Vienna. They reported the effect of carbohydrate-rich diets on non-diabetic patients. The article set Dr. Sansum thinking along radical new lines.

Next morning he consulted his new dietitian, Miss Ruth Bowden, who had recently replaced his former dietitian, Florence Smith, forced to retire because of illness. Miss Bowden had taken her dietetic internship in the Michael Reese Hospital in Chicago, and later was the dietitian at Mt. Zion Hospital in San Francisco where she had worked under the medical director, Dr. Samuel Hurwitz, the first doctor in San Francisco to try out the insulin from Lilly. She had been well-trained in the accepted type of diet for diabetic patients. Dr. Sansum was now proposing to change from the classic high fat starvation diet to a higher carbohydrate diet, a complete reversal of the standard methods. Although slightly apprehensive, Miss Bowden said she was willing to experiment.

Charles Cowan happened to be in Santa Barbara for observation at the time, so Dr. Sansum decided to use his most celebrated patient as the guinea pig for his radical new diet theories. He gave Cowan a diet of the same caloric value as he was accustomed to, but with a ration of two grams of carbohydrate to one gram of fat. The diet contained an adequate amount of fruit, potatoes, other vegetables, and bread and milk.

Cowan's response to this new diet was so strikingly favorable — he called it his "first square meal in years" — that Dr. Sansum decided to try it on the gentleman from Denver who complained of lack of energy. His response matched Cowan's; he regained his vigor and ambition almost at once and returned to Colorado to pick up his normal work load again.

When the success of the new diet had been demonstrated beyond reasonable doubt with his own patients, Dr. Sansum wrote a paper and submitted it to Morris Fishbein, the crusty editor of the *Journal* of the American Medical Association, or JAMA as it was known in the profession. It was accepted immediately and appeared in the January 1926 issue. Simultaneously and independently, Aldersberg and Porges, his colleagues in Austria, published an almost parallel report of their findings regarding the effect of high carbohydrate diets on diabetic patients, and the theory and practice of what the Viennese research team called a "curative treatment" of the disease.

Dr. Sansum's widely-circulated report, titled "The Use of High Carbohydrate Diets in the Treatment of Diabetes Mellitus," was also signed by N. R. Blatherwick, Ph.D. and Ruth Bowden, B.S.

During 1925 more than 200 patients were put on the new dietary regimen, and in each case all traces of the diabetic type of acidosis were eliminated. Foods formerly on the banned list, such as bread, fruit, potatoes and milk, were now available to diabetics.

"I believe this method of treatment will reduce the death rate from diabetes to zero!" exulted Dr. Sansum in his annual report to the directors of Cottage Hospital. Rarely had he ever resorted to such superlative language.

Sansum, Blatherwick and Bowden wrote another scholarly paper on the new diet for the AMA *Journal*, which they summarized as follows:

> (1) With the use of high carbohydrate diets, we have found no difficulty in keeping patients sugar-free and with normal blood sugar.

> (2) The patients are restored to a more nearly normal state of physical and mental activity.

> (3) The patients are freed from the slightest traces of the acetone type of acidosis.

> (4) The potatoes, milk and fruits have enabled us to eliminate the acid-ash type of acidosis which we believe has been a cause of the high incidence of blood vessel disease in diabetics.

> (5) The diets are more palatable.

> (6) The patients lose their craving for forbidden foods, especially for

the carbohydrates.

(7) A somewhat lower caloric intake is apparently required for full maintenance.

(8) These diets are cheaper, because they contain no special foods and much less of the expensive fats, such as cream, butter and olive oil.

(9) Theoretically, at least, and because of the entire freedom from acidosis, such diets should afford the patients the best opportunity for partial recovery.

This JAMA article was enthusiastically received by the medical profession at large and certainly by the nation's diabetes patients. It set in motion a world-wide application of the new carbohydrate diet for diabetics which is the basis of diets in use to the present day, more than half a century after its introduction in the United States by Dr. Sansum. In some respects this was his greatest contribution to his profession.

For the past year Dr. Sansum had assigned three laboratory workers full time to the problem of purifying insulin. This unusually difficult problem was of fundamental importance if the exact chemical nature of the drug was ever to be ascertained.

The Potter laboratory was obtaining a much higher yield of insulin from its raw material than the Eli Lilly Company had so far achieved. Only a year before, Sansum and Blatherwick had been pleased over a maximum yield of 400 standard rabbit units per kilogram of pancreatic glands; by the end of 1924 the same amount of material was yielding 2,000 units. Among other benefits, this scientific achievement resulted in another sharp reduction in the cost of insulin to the consumer.

Dr. Sansum said in his annual report:

"Our clinic's first series of preliminary experiments in the production of high blood pressure in rabbits, with its accompanying diseases of the blood vessels and kidneys, are now finished and have been convincingly successful. We believe that this is the first time in medical history that high blood pressure and its associated complications have been produced in the laboratory. The fact that this was accomplished by a diet error — resorting to the old-fashioned high fat starvation diet we used for so many years in which acid-ash foods predominated — should have a wider clinical application both in the prevention and treatment of diabetes.

"A modern hospital is not only interested in the immediate relief of sickness, but also in its prevention. This is the function of the research department. Too few people realize the value of this unpublicized phase of hospital work. Vital statistics show that the average length of life in the United States is on the increase. This has been accomplished primarily through the efforts of hospitals and research laboratories. We would like to interest more people in supporting our research endeavors in Santa Barbara."

Dr. Sansum's appeal did not fall on deaf ears. During the year, as news of what Sansum and his staff were accomplishing in the Potter Wing gained wider currency, thirty-one donors contributed $33,316.96 to the Potter Metabolic Clinic to carry on the good work.

8

The Merger with Cottage Hospital

A major earthquake shook Santa Barbara at 6:42 on the morning of Monday, June 29, 1925. In the space of a dozen clock ticks the city's main thoroughfare, State Street, found itself flanked by dust-smoking windrows of rubble, from Sola Street on the north to the foot of Stearns Wharf. Thirteen lives had been snuffed out — an incredibly small toll for a population numbering 25,000 — and more than $15,000,000 worth of property was destroyed.

Due to its sturdy steel and concrete construction, Cottage Hospital and Dr. Sansum's Potter Wing survived with only minimal plaster cracks and a toppled chimney or two. The city's other hospitals, St. Francis and County General, suffered heavy damage and their patients had to be transferred to Cottage.

Staff personnel and such ambulatory patients as could manage helped in moving out Cottage Hospital patients, around 75 of them, to cots and tents set up on the grounds. There they spent the day, until safety inspectors had checked out the buildings and pronounced them safe against aftershocks, of which more than a thousand were registered during the coming week.

"Dr. Sansum was immensely proud of how his staff performed the day of the big shake," nurse Mildred Root Lewis recalled more than fifty years later. "Even though gas was shut off in the diet kitchen, not one of Dr. Sansum's patients missed a meal. The chef set up a huge soup kettle out in the yard and fed all the hospital patients. The diabetic patients got their trays promptly for breakfast, luncheon and supper, which was remarkable inasmuch as diabetic diets had to be weighed out gram by gram."

Two male diabetic patients volunteered for courier duty during the day, making numerous round trips to Ventura, twenty-five miles away, to send and pick up telegrams, since all wires were down in Santa Barbara. The only communication to the outside world in the first few hectic hours came from two ham radio operators, Graham George and Brandon Wentworth, who set up a makeshift wireless station in the center of State Street and relayed messages to ships at sea.

By nightfall, electricity had been restored at Cottage Hospital, although most of the city was without power and light. The patients were moved back indoors. Whenever the Edison Company had to cut the power during the night the hospital staff received enough warning to prepare kerosene lamps and candles.

An especially severe aftershock jolted the stricken city at 1:22 the next morning and several patients asked to be carried outdoors again. One of Dr. Sansum's patients, Murray Vail, positioned his automobile at the curb so that its lights could reassure the patients that all was well.

On the credit side of the ledger, the disaster leveled

hundreds of Santa Barbara's substandard buildings so they had to be demolished for reasons of public safety. Farsighted citizens seized upon this providential opportunity to rebuild their city in a more beautiful image. City officials drew up strict building codes and zoning laws and organized an Architectural Board of Review with enough clout to enforce regulations that new construction had to conform to a Hispanic-Mediterranean style of architecture for which Santa Barbara was to gain world renown in years to come.

(It is interesting to note that Santa Barbara's architectural renaissance was born in the work of a newcomer, Bernhard Hoffman, whose original reason for settling in Santa Barbara had been to put his daughter Margaret, a diabetic, into the Potter Clinic for treatment. Hoffman's construction in 1920 of the popular tourist attraction known as El Paseo and its adjoining Street in Spain, and his restoration of historic Casa de la Guerra facing the town plaza, set planning guidelines for the Hispanic-style construction which rose in the wake of the earthquake.)

The disruptions in routine caused by the big shake and its almost daily after-temblors, which kept hundreds of nervous families eating and sleeping in their back yards all that summer, made the manufacture of insulin a doubly onerous chore. Providentially, it was at this point that Eli Lilly & Company began supplying enough standardized, high-potency insulin to enable Dr. Sansum to halt his manufacturing program permanently. He dismantled his extraction facilities both in Los Angeles and Santa Barbara. After five years of predawn visits to slaughterhouses, gruelling round trips to Los Angeles, and tedious extraction and assay work in the laboratory, Dr. Sansum was only too glad to announce the passing of Santa Barbara's historic "insulin era."

The change-over to Iletin (insulin Lilly) released badly-needed manpower for other laboratory work. During 1925 Drs. Sansum and Blatherwick concentrated their staff activities on methods for purifying insulin. The major accomplishment of the year, however, involved a landmark project conducted by a brilliant young chemist from Beruit, Lebanon, Melville Sahyun, who perfected a method of standardizing insulin so as to determine its relative potency.

Following the discovery of insulin in 1921 in Toronto, all firms licensed to manufacture the substance in the United States were required to send samples of each batch of their product to Dr. Sansum and other American "referees" for testing before the University of Toronto would grant permission for production to proceed. To pass these tests, each batch had to be measured against a standard.

Two methods had been devised for standardizing commercial insulin. The first, originating in Toronto with Macleod and Orr, involved the average decrease in blood sugar in test rabbits over a period of five hours after the subcutaneous injection of insulin was given the animals. The second method, the one used by Lilly & Company, was based on the incidence of convulsions in a group of several hundred rabbits injected with graded doses of insulin, the unit dose being considered the smallest amount required to produce convulsions in three out of every four rabbits.

Sahyun's method of measuring insulin potency proved vastly superior to the two methods then in use, involving the production of convulsions in test rabbits which occurred at a blood sugar level of about thirty milligrams per hundred cubic centimeters. Sahyun's method had the advantage of reducing testing time from an average of a month to just under 24 hours maximum. When he published his paper describing the method, in collaboration with Dr. Blatherwick, in the May 1926 issue of the *American Journal of Physiology,* Sahyun's method was quickly adopted by scientists and is in general use to the present day.

Dr. Sansum's on-going studies of high carbohydrate diets in the treatment of diabetes mellitus, and his daily lectures and classroom demonstrations for his patients, led to the preparation and publication of a 75-page booklet, "Instructions for Diabetic Patients," co-authored by Dr. Sansum, dietitian Ruth Bowden, and laboratory assistant John A. Berger, the latter a diabetic who was proving an invaluable assistant in the clinic laboratory. This handbook accompanied every patient who was discharged from the Potter Clinic diabetes program, along with a hypodermic syringe and a supply of insulin for home use.

During the "earthquake year," as 1925 came to be known forever after in Santa Barbara, Dr. Sansum's preliminary experiments in various fields were fast making him a national celebrity. One of his most ardent admirers was Arthur Brisbane, roving editor for the Hearst newspaper chain, who often devoted considerable space in his daily column to the accomplishments of the man he dubbed "Santa Barbara's genius." Whenever the noted journalist came to town he wrote his column late at night in the city room of the Santa Barbara *Daily News* overlooking De la Guerra Plaza, now the *News-Press* building. He would either telephone Dr. Sansum to get the latest progress reports on American diabetes research, or visit the Potter Metabolic Clinic to see for himself.

Franklin K. Lane, the Secretary of the Interior in President Wilson's cabinet, in an article published in the San Francisco *News,* made this comment:

> "Major Max C. Fleischmann [president of General Foods and a steady contributor to the Cottage Hospital building fund] and Dr.

William D. Sansum, both of Santa Barbara, should be listed high among the real rulers of California. They are outstanding figures of their type and character, representing the principal interests that form the basis of prosperity and happiness in the Golden State."

The Hon. John Murphy, a prominent political figure in Wisconsin during the 1920s, was quoted by the United Press as saying that "Dr. Sansum of Santa Barbara is a nationally known medical authority, second in prominence in this country only to the Mayo Brothers of Rochester, Minnesota." This was the highest accolade the press could bestow upon a medical man at that time.

Sansum, appearing oblivious to such publicity, patterned his simple life around his laboratory, his daily hospital rounds, and his ongoing lectures to patients and staff.

The pastor of the First Congregational Church of Santa Barbara, hearing that Dr. Sansum had belonged to that denomination as a youth in Wisconsin, made frequent overtures to lure the good doctor into a pew on Sundays, but with only sporadic success.

"I am basically a religious man," Dr. Sansum was quoted by his son Donald, "but since I work from dawn to dark six days a week, it is imperative that I relax on the Sabbath. I do so in the most sublime cathedral God ever created for His worship — the great out of doors."

One of Sansum's favorite places for this Sunday "worship," because of its proximity to his home, was the oak-dappled hilly region southwest of the city known as Hope Ranch. Historically the Mexican land grant of Las Positas y Calera of 1843, the area became the sheep-grazing range of a pioneer settler named Thomas Hope. In the 1880s it was the proposed site of a luxury hotel to be built by the Southern Pacific Railroad, a hotel which failed to materialize.

A speculator from New York, Maurice Heckscher, had acquired Hope Ranch the year before Dr. Sansum arrived in Santa Barbara. The ranch was managed for Heckscher by James Edwards, a former lieutenant in Canada's famous Princess Pat Regiment during World War I. He had been gassed at Ypres and was in the care of Dr. Sansum for his war-related health problems, as a result of which the two became close friends.

One of the features of Hope Ranch was Laguna Blanca, a 32-acre private lake which Heckscher kept stocked with black bass for the benefit of his coterie of sportsmen friends back East. Thanks to his friendship with superintendent Edwards, Dr. Sansum was allowed to fish this private lake whenever he chose. Usually accompanied by his laboratory assistant Loyal C. "Max" Maxwell, the two invariably brought back big catches from their Sunday jaunts to Laguna Blanca. They turned the fish over to the chef at Cottage Hospital as a welcome supplement to the patients' menus.

"I always used to clean our catches," Maxwell recalled fifty years later. "I used the sink in our insulin-manufacturing room for my fish-cleaning chores. On one weekend the laboratory was not available, so I used an adjoining room which, on rare occasions, was used for autopsies. One Sunday night I was in a hurry to get somewhere and forgot to tidy up my mess after cleaning the fish. As luck would have it, that very night they had to use the room for a post mortem examination. The chief nurse was furious at the condition I had left the room in and next morning Mr. Curtis, the hospital superintendent, called me on the carpet. Fortunately for me Dr. Sansum intervened and smoothed things over, and I was dismissed with a warning never to do it again."

In addition to fishing, sparsely-settled Hope Ranch

provided a fine hunting-ground for quail and doves, and superintendent Edwards opened the game preserve for Dr. Sansum whenever he chose to take his shotgun off the rack. This sport came to an end, however, when a corporation headed by realtor Harold G. Chase purchased Hope Ranch from Heckscher and began developing it into a first-class suburb which eventually would rival Montecito for the elegance of its mansions and formal gardens. The builder of one of Hope Ranch Park's earliest and most stately residences was William R. Dickinson whose daughter Nancy was one of Dr. Sansum's first twenty recipients of insulin for diabetes. In gratitude, the Dickinsons became heavy donors to Dr. Sansum's research work.

Early in 1926, following the financially disastrous year of the earthquake in which the Potter Metabolic Clinic operated at a deficit for the first time, an emergency staff meeting was called by the directors of Cottage Hospital to shore up the sagging economic status of the institution.

Dr. Sansum emerged from the meeting with disquieting news. From this time forward, he said, the Potter Metabolic Clinic would be merged with the hospital's research department, with Dr. Nuzum and himself as co-directors. The Potter name was being discontinued; the clinic would become part of what would henceforth be called the Santa Barbara Cottage Hospital Research Department. Cancer research would be conducted by Dr. Henry J. Ullmann; cardiological research by Dr. Nuzum; and metabolic research by Dr. Sansum.

While he was secretly unhappy at being reduced to a co-director under the new administrative set-up, Dr. Sansum did not let the demotion, as he called it, make any difference to his on-going clinical research programs, one of which continued to be a failure — the creation of a workable oral insulin compound.

A number of new oral compounds hit the market at that time and Sansum's laboratory subjected each one to exhaustive study, particularly myrtillin, synthalin and glukhorment. Myrtillin was made from blueberry leaves and had been introduced to America by Dr. Frederick M. Allen of the Rockefeller Institute of Medical Research in Morristown, New Jersey. This preparation was carefully tested by Sansum and Blatherwick, being given by mouth to several of his patients, but with little or no clinical effect; it did not seem to be specific in the control of the acetone type of diabetes, which it was supposed to be.

The new drug synthalin, made in Germany, was a guanidine compound which had been found effective in lowering blood sugar in test rabbits. While it reduced the total amount of sugar in the urine, Dr. Sansum's staff found it also to be dangerously poisonous. When given in doses sufficiently large to reduce blood sugar, it caused death from a severe form of kidney deterioration associated with retention of sewage products in the blood. It was also harmful to the liver.

"We at the Potter Metabolic Clinic do not feel justified in offering synthalin to human patients," Dr. Sansum and Dr. Blatherwick stated in a joint report of findings. "It has been tried in other clinics, where it has produced nausea and vomiting, sometimes associated with albumin in the urine. We believe that synthalin lowers blood sugar and reduces urine sugar simply because it is toxic to the tissues, rather than because it is really burning any sugar."

Glukhorment, another German preparation, said to be made from the pancreatic gland by fermentation, was not as toxic as synthalin; it did lower blood and urine sugar; but the action of this controversial preparation resembled that of synthalin so strongly that Dr. Sansum refused to give it orally to his patients.

"We are continuing our own experiments," Sansum

and Blatherwick reported, "hoping to obtain a non-toxic substance which will be of value to diabetic patients when taken by mouth. So far the hydrochloric acid in the stomach has nullified the insulin on contact. We have prepared a number of guanidine compounds (a product of protein hydrolysis) similar to synthalin, but none of these has so far proved suitable for clinical use, in our opinion.'

Dr. Sansum's professional rejection of the new oral preparations was shared by most of his colleagues in the United States, resulting in their removal from the shelves of American drugstores. The protection of the public by pre-testing new pharmaceuticals was, in Dr. Sansum's view, one of the most important functions of the research scientist.

The mounting work load, the added anxieties caused by the administrative shake-up at the hospital, and his reluctance to take a real vacation were beginning to take their toll on Dr. Sansum as he reached his mid-forties.

However dedicated he was, Dr. Sansum was a practical man. He knew if he continued to drive himself at the pace he had maintained in the five years since coming to Santa Barbara, he would break down.

What was indicated, friends told him, was a weekend retreat, a hideaway where he could find release from the pressures and stresses of his professional responsibilities. Thus, in what was probably the nick of time, something new and exciting entered Dr. Sansum's life — a savior bearing the melodic Spanish name of Casa del Mar, House of the Sea.

9

Genesis of the
Sansum Clinic

Casa del Mar, despite its romantic name, was a nondescript, weather-stained board-and-bat beach shack perched on the brink of a seacliff between Goleta and Coal Oil Points, on the coast eight miles west of Santa Barbara. The First National Bank of Santa Barbara closed the escrow for Dr. Sansum in February of 1926.

The beach house, known as the Coolidge property, occupied the south end of two narrow, elongated lots fronting on 6717 Del Playa Drive in a moribund subdivision called Isla Vista. Due to poor soil and lack of good water, lot sales were not brisk.

Over forty years later, when Isla Vista had become a congested bedroom community for UCSB, it had unwelcome notoriety thrust upon it when it became the scene of so-called "student riots" in which the I.V. branch of the Bank of America was burned down by radical elements of the hippie-type "street people," ostensibly to punish the bank and the "establishment" for their support of the Vietnam war. But in 1926, Isla Vista was isolated and virtually deserted, reached by a sandy road from Goleta — an ideal place for an exhausted doctor to have a retreat for his rest and recreation.

Dr. Sansum took to spending more and more of his spare time at Casa del Mar, planting cypress trees to go with existing eucalyptuses, building a boarded-in water tank tower adjacent to the street, and a flight of stairs leading down the fifty-foot shale cliff to his private beach which offered such diversions as sunbathing, surf fishing, swimming, sailing and just plain beachcombing.

The idyllic hours at Casa del Mar fortified Dr. Sansum for his mounting work load at the Clinic. In the subject closest to his heart — the role of controlled diet in diabetes treatment — his work during 1927 convinced Dr. Sansum that high blood pressure and its attendant complications may have been due to the old diabetic diets made up largely of bran breads, meat and eggs.

"We hope to prove shortly," Dr. Sansum said, "that our new diets, with ample amounts of fruits, vegetables and milk, should prevent hypertensive problems in our diabetes patients."

In treating the various types of indigestion which diabetic patients suffered, Dr. Sansum had the pharmaceutical house of Parke Davis & Company manufacture a special enteric-coated pancreatin tablet to his specifications. This tablet was usually specific when the pancreas failed to make a sufficient amount of its own digestive secretions. This alleviated a common ailment of diabetic patients whose pancreatic cells which secreted digestive juices were partially atrophied or destroyed, along with the islands of Langerhans whose function it was to provide sugar-burning insulin.

Because of Dr. Sansum's research into the relationship of diet to health, in 1925 he published a small book entitled "The Normal Diet" for the mutual use of physicians and patients. He revised the book in 1927 and over 10,000 copies were sold, much to the displeasure of the local Medical Society Ethics Committee, who branded it "personal advertising."

In 1928 Harper Brothers published a hard-cover volume titled "The Treatment of Diabetes Mellitus with Higher Carbohydrate Diets." This work, one of Harper's "Medical Monograph" series, carried the by-lines of Dr. Sansum, Dr. Percy Gray and Ruth Bowden B.S. In 1939 this manual was revised by Dr. Sansum, Dr. Alfred E. Koehler and Miss Bowden.

Dr. Sansum was much interested in an educational program for patients, whom he required to attend classes and have individual instruction for future home care. These classes were later expanded to include all patients in Cottage Hospital, with assistance from various members of the local Medical Society. They were open to the public in the evening, and at first were held in the auditorium of the new Knapp School of Nursing which philanthropist George Owen Knapp had built at Bath and Junipero Streets as a memorial to his wife, Louise Savage Knapp.

The lecture series initiated by Dr. Sansum in the 1920s is still being continued at Cottage Hospital. For awhile they were given in the new Bissell Auditorium, built next to the Potter Wing by Dr. and Mrs. Elmer Bissell in memory of their son and daughter. When it was torn down to make way for new construction, the lectures, including a series for the parents of diabetic children conducted by Dr. Donald E. McMillan and other guest lecturers, were given in the Burtness Auditorium of the new hospital.

That era in American history referred to as the "Coolidge Prosperity" years had seen Dr. Sansum establish himself on a firm financial footing, more than compensating him and Mrs. Sansum for their long years of sacrifice and deprivation while he was going though medical school in Chicago. Mrs. Sansum, while active in affairs of the Santa Barbara City Club and the Marguerite Chapter, Order of the Eastern Star, did not impose a heavy social schedule on her husband. Their son Donald was now in his active teenage years, with special interests in horseback riding and sports, mainly tennis. By now the Sansum residence at 2301 Hollister Avenue was becoming too cramped for the family's expanding activities.

Clearly, more spacious quarters were needed. Accordingly, the family set out on a series of Sunday afternoon tours of Santa Barbara and Montecito, looking for a homesite to build on. By now the Dodge sedan had been replaced by a yellow Pierce-Arrow limousine for Mrs. Sansum and a more humble Ford V-8 for Dr. Sansum.

The Hollister Estate Company, founded in 1868 by Col. W. W. Hollister, Santa Barbara's leading pioneer of the Victorian era, had subdivided the Samarkand Hills immediately west of Oak Park and the Cottage Hospital neighborhood. This subdivision was dominated by the Persian-style edifice and grounds of Dr. Prynce Hopkins' former "Boyland," an elite boys' school. Dr. Hopkins' pacifistic leanings during World War I had sent him into self-imposed exile abroad and his boys' school had been converted into the luxurious Samarkand Hotel, catering to winter visitors.

A block east of the Samarkand Hotel was a one and three-quarter acre view lot overlooking Santa Barbara, owned by the secretary of the Hollister Estate Company, Ed Tallant. The Sansums purchased this property from Tallant on March 6, 1926. Three years later, at what is now designated as 2800 Tallant Road, they built an elegant home, tile-roofed in the accepted

Santa Barbara mode, surrounded by beautifully-landscaped grounds which included a secluded guest house, a small riding stable, and a private enclosed tennis court for Donald and his friends. In the words of the *Morning Press*, "the spacious new Sansum estate is worthy of inclusion in the galaxy of beautiful homes usually associated with Montecito or the recent residences going up in Hope Ranch Park."

The year 1928 was not one of unalloyed delight for Dr. Sansum, however. During the eight years he had been at the helm of the Potter Metabolic Clinic, his chief financial backer had been the Carnegie Corporation, which had supported the Clinic from the time of its founding by Dr. Potter in New York in 1916.

Now the Carnegie Corporation, through its president Dr. Henry Pritchett, advised Dr. Sansum that Mr. Carnegie was shifting the focus of his philanthropy from medicine to education, and that the 1929 allotment would be the thirteenth and last annual Carnegie contribution to the Potter Metabolic Clinic.

This pending dry-up of the Carnegie pipeline brought immediate fiscal policy changes at Cottage Hospital. The trustees, hard on the heels of the Carnegie announcement, informed Dr. Sansum that while he would continue to enjoy the free use of their facilities and a private office (as ordered by the wealthy donors of the Potter Wing), his annual salary of $12,000 was ending immediately.

Staff changes were also resulting from the merger of the Potter Clinic with the hospital's research department. Dr. Blatherwick, in part influenced by Carnegie's forthcoming withdrawal from research funding, resigned to become chief of research for the Metropolitan Life Insurance Company of New York. The assistant he had brought out from Yale University, Dr. Marion Bell, also resigned, leaving the animal work she had been doing to her young assistant, Melville Sahyun.

Dr. Blatherwick was succeeded as head of the research department by a young biochemist named Fritz Bischoff, Ph.D., who was destined to make important contributions to insulin research which were instrumental in winning many future financial grants for the hospital.

Dr. Sansum's fishing partner and Dr. Blatherwick's laboratory expert in insulin manufacture, Loyal C. Maxwell, resigned to continue his work for a doctorate at the University of California in Berkeley.

Directly due to the merger, Dr. Sansum's chief dietitian, Ruth Bowden, was also leaving. Changes were to be made in the dietetic department, and eventually the diet kitchen in the Potter Metabolic Clinic would be absorbed into the central kitchen of the hospital. However, Miss Bowden had seen the new high carbohydrate diet plan safely inaugurated before any radical changes were put into effect.

All these personnel changes disturbed Dr. Sansum, apart from the fact that his pride was stung by finding himself a co-director in the research department with Dr. Nuzum, instead of the chief of an autonomous operation.

He feared that the continuation of his main projects, insulin refinement and diabetes research, might be in jeopardy under the new administrative set-up. What if other departments — Dr. Ullmann's cancer, Dr. Nuzum's cardiology — obtained priority over the metabolic work in progress? Money would have to be raised elsewhere. Two of Dr. Sansum's most generous benefactors in the past, Major Max C. Fleischmann and Edward Harkness, had just donated $200,000 each toward building a new hospital wing, caused indirectly by the acceleration of Dr. Sansum's patient census; they could not be asked to contribute to further diabetes research at this time.

Personality conflicts began to manifest themselves

among the staff personnel, something that was unheard of in the old days. A diversion came during this uneasy period, in the form of a 1928 visit from a distinguished man of medicine, Prof. J.J.R. Macleod of the University of Toronto, the man who had provided Banting and Best with the facilities they needed in 1921, resulting in the discovery of insulin. Macleod was now an exchange professor at Stanford University in Palo Alto, and was spending his Easter vacation in Santa Barbara. He was especially interested in Melville Sahyun's work in standardizing insulin.

It astonished Prof. Macleod that Dr. Sansum's talented young Lebanese chemist possessed only a bachelor of arts degree. He urged Sahyun to enroll at Stanford and go for a doctor's degree. Upon learning that Sahyun had never depancreatized a laboratory animal, Prof. Macleod had a dog sent in and, using Sahyun's laboratory bench for an operating table, instructed the young chemist in the surgical techniques needed to remove the animal's pancreas and render it diabetic, a most useful tool for young Sahyun's future experiments in the treatment of human diabetes mellitus.

The year had seen significant advances in insulin research emanating from Dr. Sansum's laboratory. In the past it had been generally believed that adrenalin was antagonistic to the action of insulin. Sansum's staff demonstrated in the laboratory that this was an erroneous premise. Adrenalin and insulin were demonstrated to be antagonistic toward blood sugar. This was proved in the laboratory by studying the action of insulin on rabbits whose adrenal glands had been ligated. These animals showed a remarkably uniform tolerance to insulin, proving that the great variation of animals (and reasoning by analogy, of people) is immediately concerned with adrenalin activity. A spin-off of this discovery was the opening up of a new method of insulin assay.

During the year, Dr. Sansum finally decided to abandon attempts to perfect an oral insulin. (Half a century later this problem still remains unresolved.)

In September 1928, Melville Sahyun, following Dr. Macleod's advice, resigned after five years of distinguished work under Dr. Sansum to enroll at Stanford University in pursuit of higher degrees. Dr. Sahyun went on to a brilliant professional career in Chicago, including advanced work in the development of slow-acting insulin. He eventually returned to Santa Barbara to build and operate his own laboratories.

The growing threat to the financing of his private diabetes research, aggravated by the gradual diminution of his staff, combined to force Dr. Sansum into making a critically important career decision in the autumn of 1928.

While he would continue to use the hospital facilities, he would hire his own staff of top-notch medical specialists, including at least one physician with a strong interest in diabetes research, and establish a private clinic.

Out of that decision, forged in the hot fires of necessity, came what was destined to be one of the most highly respected medical institutions in the country — the Sansum Medical Clinic.

10

Bad News from Wall Street

"A private clinic," Dr. Sansum was wont to tell anyone who would listen that fateful year of 1928, "can be no better than the caliber of its professional staff. I intend to hire the best available men in their respective fields."

His first selection was an old friend and associate, Dr. Robert A. Hare, who had served his internship at Cottage Hospital and then went back to the University of Chicago and Rush Medical School as a lecturer. Dr. Hare gladly accepted an invitation to join the cadre of the fledgling Sansum Clinic, early in 1929.

Dr. Hare was an older man, upon whom Sansum would rely heavily for advice and guidance, both in professional and business matters, in the trying years which lay ahead.

One of Dr. Sansum's own interns, Dr. Percival Allen Gray, was his second staff selection. Dr. Gray, newly arrived in Santa Barbara, had received his medical degree from Rush in 1927. Although only twenty-eight, he was already a recognized authority on diabetes.

For some time Dr. Sansum had kept an interested eye on another intern, Dr. Delbert H. McNamara, a native of Washington State and one of the first doctors in Santa Barbara to become an expert in the new science of electrocardiography. Two years previously Dr. McNamara had married another M.D., Doris Erkenbeck of San Diego. Dr. Sansum invited this husband and wife team to join his charter staff at Sansum Clinic, and they accepted. For the important post of business administrator, Dr. Sansum dipped into the past to choose a former pupil of his from the Richmond, Wisconsin schools, Freeman T. Spinney.

Since dietetics played such an important part in Dr. Sansum's treatment of diabetes, he strongly desired to bring back his former dietitian, Ruth Bowden, to add to his professional staff. She had worked with him in inaugurating the higher carbohydrate diets for diabetic patients. He wrote her in New York and she accepted his offer to return to her old position, arriving in Santa Barbara on August 1, 1928, the same day that Dr. Hare returned from Chicago.

The Sansum Clinic began its existence in ground floor quarters of the Potter Metabolic Wing of Cottage Hospital. Extensive remodeling had to be done to provide doctors' offices and examining rooms, alterations which included glassing in the front veranda where America's first recipients of insulin had often gathered to compare notes in the early days of the Potter Clinic.

There were a few doctors in Santa Barbara who expressed resentment because Dr. Sansum was allowed the rent-free use of facilities at Cottage Hospital. Also sharing this largesse was Dr. Nuzum, who had the free use of a hospital wing for his cardiac work, and Dr

Ullmann, with his X-ray department.

The reason why this trio of doctors was so favored was easily explained. Santa Barbara Cottage Hospital was being heavily subsidized by philanthropists such as Knapp, Billings, Fleischmann, Harkness, Peabody and others. The hospital trustees could hardly dispute the donors' prerogative to offer free space for the research activities and private practices of Drs. Sansum, Nuzum, and Ullmann, if they so desired.

Dr. Sansum, like all dedicated scientists, rejoiced in the professional achievements of other diabetes researchers, especially if they were "Sansum alumni" from earlier years. He kept special track of his former chief chemist, Dr. Blatherwick, who was doing significant studies as head of the laboratories of the Metropolitan Life Insurance Company, his learned papers appearing regularly in the medical journals.

Blatherwick's assistant in the Potter laboratory, Loyal C. Maxwell, came back to Santa Barbara in 1929 with a Ph.D. from UC Berkeley. He went to work in the Cottage Hospital research department to develop a means of slowing down the action of insulin in the body. In the early 1920s when insulin was less pure, the effectiveness of a single dose lasted only eight hours at most. The impurities in this pioneer insulin sometimes caused disagreeable skin allergies in the patient, hence all pharmaceutical houses began purifying their insulin to a crystalline degree.

When word got around that Dr. Sansum had organized a private clinic, more patients came from out-of-town or out-of-state than Cottage Hospital could accommodate. Other Santa Barbara physicians, who drew their business from the local area, watched enviously as Dr. Sansum began having to seek bedrooms for his patients outside the hospital.

He turned first to the Samarkand Hotel, only a block from his new home. When that hostelry's available space was booked, he made similar arrangements with El Encanto Hotel on the Riviera hill overlooking historic Mission Santa Barbara. Later Dr. Sansum added the downtown hotel and private cottages of El Mirasol, the former villa of Christian and Albert Herter. Even the posh Santa Barbara Biltmore on the beach in Montecito began renting rooms to Dr. Sansum's diabetic out-patients.

Since most diabetes patients remained in Santa Barbara for several months, the above-named hotels found it expedient to hire trained dietitians to assist their regular chefs in preparing the special meals prescribed by Dr. Sansum — the high carbohydrate menus which patients found so palatable and nutritious.

Whether he wanted to be or not, Dr. Sansum was a news-maker. His activities in the community generated frequent headlines, again to the discomfiture of the Ethics Committee of the Medical Society which sought to insulate its membership from publicity of any kind, deeming this to be "self-advertising."

A typical example was a Santa Barbara newspaper editorial which applauded Dr. Sansum's economic value to the community, putting this ahead of the humanistic aspects of his work:

> "Dr. Sansum has done much for humanity in the few years that he has been in Santa Barbara, and he and the institution with which he is connected and those who have faith in its work, have done a great deal to advertise Santa Barbara to a class of wealthy citizens who would not have

been drawn here by any other means.

"Hundreds of people have been attracted to Santa Barbara by Dr. Sansum . . . Many have remained here; all are spending large sums here with the hotels, boarding houses and other institutions of the city. Recently F. G. Bonfils, publisher of the Denver *Post*, declared 'Every city in the country should have a Sansum system for the good it would do humanity.' . . . That is the opinion of a man who has made millions of dollars and is considered a hard-headed business man. He has taken treatments [from Dr. Sansum] and has brought his family here for treatments, so knows whereof he speaks.

"But, the wealth that has been drawn here is not all the good that Dr. Sansum has done," the editor added as if by after-thought. "Hundreds will give testimony to the treatments given where no money was exchanged, for rich and poor alike are the beneficiaries of what Dr. Sansum and his associates have to offer, and many of the poor are never asked to pay. It is because of this work of mercy, as well as for the wealth they have attracted here, that Dr. Sansum and his associates are entitled to our gratitude.

"Dr. Sansum is no doubt held in high esteem by his fellow citizens generally, but his worth to the

community is undoubtedly appreciated more fully by those in many
other places who have benefited from
his services. Santa Barbara is under a
debt of gratitude to him for the work
that he has done in behalf of
humanity as a citizen of Santa
Barbara, as well as for the wealth he
has attracted here through the
services he offers the ailing."

It was at this period that an important personality
entered Dr. Sansum's life — Hildahl I. Burtness, M.D.
Born of Norwegian parentage on a farm near Blooming
Prairie, Minnesota, Burtness graduated from St. Olaf
College in Northfield, Minnesota, where he was a
football star. He enrolled at Dr. Sansum's *alma mater*,
Rush Medical College of the University of Chicago,
where Dean Ernest Irons first told him about Dr.
Sansum and his diabetes research at the Santa Barbara
Cottage Hospital. It was as a young medical student
that Burtness met his future wife, Miss Luella Malberg.

Young Dr. Burtness' decision to devote his career to
the treatment and research of diabetes was motivated by
the strongest personal reasons. His mother, grand-
father, three aunts, four uncles and a brother suffered
from the hereditary disease.

Through the influence of Dean Irons, Dr. Burtness
obtained an internship at the Santa Barbara Cottage
Hospital. Driving his Model T Ford coupe, he crossed
the country from Chicago and arrived in Santa Barbara
on June 30, 1929, the day he met the man who was to
become his mentor and closest friend in the profession,
Dr. W. D. Sansum.

The following day Dr. Burtness started his
internship. He sent for his fiancee Luella to come to
Santa Barbara, and the couple were married on August

124

23, 1929. They have raised three sons, George L., William C., and Robert Alan Burtness.

It was at this time that Dr. Sansum's original contact with Santa Barbara, multimillionaire George Owen Knapp, commented that he was astonished by the volume of out-of-town patients arriving daily at the Potter Wing.

"You can't go on like this," Knapp said. "Cottage Hospital can't provide you with adequate clinic and laboratory space. Your work is being hindered, and your work is too important. Why don't you erect your own clinic building?"

Dr. Sansum thought over this startling suggestion. "But where?" he asked. "I would have to be near the hospital, and there isn't much vacant land to be had around here."

Knapp said, "I own most of the frontage on West Pueblo Street across from the hospital. In fact, I am building a private office for Dr. Nuzum at the corner of Pueblo and Bath. I could sell you the adjoining frontage at 317 West Pueblo for a clinic."

Knapp's proposal fired Sansum's blood with new enthusiasm. Why *not* build his own clinic? He could afford it. Times were booming. A burgeoning patient census had boosted his yearly income — he once told a staff member that he was netting more than $100,000 a year — and his stocks and bonds were appreciating in value. He was not dependent upon the local community for his clientele, as most of his colleagues were. Diabetics were checking in at the Potter Wing from all over the world, and their numbers would likely increase in the future, thanks in part to Santa Barbara's famous scenery and year-round climate, advantages which other clinics could not match.

Working at night at home, Dr. Sansum began making rough sketches of a two-story clinic building with basement which could fit the three fifty-foot lots offered him by Knapp at an uninflated figure. In order to take full advantage of the expertise of his associates, Sansum photostated his floor plans and circulated them among his staff, inviting their suggestions and criticisms.

Carleton M. Winslow, one of Santa Barbara's leading architects, was engaged to design the new Sansum Clinic building, incorporating Dr. Sansum's pet ideas and those winnowed from his staff's suggestions. Architect Winslow agreed with his client that the new Sansum Clinic should match the clean Italianate style of the Cottage Hospital. Other than that, Dr. Sansum had only one instruction for his architect: "Keep everything spacious. Hallways, examination rooms, public lobby, laboratories, restrooms. All my career I have had to work in cramped quarters. I want my people to have elbow room and plenty of it."

Working through the Knapp Fund, a foundation of which George Owen Knapp was nominally the vice president, Dr. Sansum purchased three lots from Knapp and another from George C. Sloan, to give him a 205-foot frontage on the south side of Pueblo Street between Bath and Castillo, adjoining the Nuzum Building. The lots extended southward to Encinal Avenue, a mid-block alley.

In a ferment of enthusiasm, Dr. Sansum sent word back home in Baraboo for his youngest brother, John Sansum, to come to California and take over the permanent job of assistant manager, maintenance superintendent and groundskeeper for the new clinic. John did so, moving his family into the cottage at the corner of Hollister and Pueblo, only a block away, which Dr. Sansum had vacated upon completion of his new home near the Samarkand Hotel. John's son Lavanne grew up to become a prominent Los Angeles doctor.

The architect's plans for the new clinic were cleared by the Santa Barbara City building department with a minimum of delay, not always easy in a city which was vigilantly enforcing a radical new concept of unified Hispanic architecture following the 1925 earthquake.

Across the street, a $500,000 surgical wing and maternity unit was going up, thanks to the benevolence of Max C. Fleischmann. It was the latest in a series of major building programs undertaken by Cottage Hospital. (Major Fleischmann's wife, Sarah, was one of Dr. Sansum's diabetes patients.)

Despite his preoccupation with building his new clinic, Dr. Sansum stepped up, rather than diminished his personal work load at Cottage Hospital. He launched a new series of seminars for doctors, nurses and diabetics and their families, using the new auditorium of the Knapp School of Nursing for the meetings.

"In the treatment of diabetes," he explained, "there are three objectives to be attained: the patient should be kept continuously free of sugar in the urine, while maintaining normal levels of blood sugar; the patient must be kept continuously free from acidosis; and the patient should be nourished as evidenced by satisfactory weight. In treating diabetes with insulin, there are four conditions that must be satisfied: first, the sugar-burning, or utilizing power of the insulin in units per cubic centimeter should be known; second, the patient's natural tolerance must be determined in grams of sugar-formers; third, the exact value of the proposed diet should be known; and lastly, the dosage of insulin may then be adjusted to make up the difference between the sugar formers of the proposed diet, and those of the patient's natural tolerance."

Thanks to Dr. Sansum's experimentation in diets for diabetics, an increasing number of less-ill patients were able to discontinue the use of insulin entirely. Dr.

Sansum's stress diet was winning him international respect, not only in the treatment of diabetes, but for persons suffering from heart disease and nephritis.

"We believe," Dr. Sansum was quoted by the press, "that the over-consumption of bread and meat, associated with the underconsumption of fruits, vegetables and milk, is one of the most important causes of high blood pressure and related complications. Patients suffering from this disease readily exchange their meats, eggs and fish for milk and milk products, but they have considerable difficulty in giving up bread. But we are solving the bread problem, too."

Ten miles southeast of Santa Barbara lies the Carpinteria Valley, known since the turn of the century as "the lima bean capitol of the world," an industry which started when a sailor aboard a windjammer tied to Stearns Wharf in Santa Barbara gave a Carpinteria farmer a ten-pound bag of large white beans he had picked up in Callao, Peru, known as "Lima beans." Climatic conditions and soil chemistry in Carpinteria match those of the Peruvian coast, with the result that lima beans soon became a local industry and an American food staple.

Dr. Sansum, analyzing the chemistry of lima beans, decided they would make a very palatable muffin by combining lima bean flour with whole wheat flour. Working with the Parma Company, a local firm, he succeeded in producing an excellent non-acid yeast bread, using the mixture of bean and wheat flour mixed with raisins and crushed walnuts — the latter being a major industry of the Goleta Valley, neighboring Santa Barbara on the west.

"Diabetes patients love lima bean bread," Dr. Sansum reported proudly. "So does the general public. Our two leading gourmet groceries, Show's and Diehl's, are stocking lima bean bread regularly, from a bakery in Ojai. We have felt at the clinic that this tasty bread will be of incalculable value in treating and preventing high blood pressure. We have felt for a long time that so valuable and nutritious a food as the lima bean does not have the universal use it should be enjoying."

Architect Winslow completed his working drawings by September. The contracting firm of Alexander McKellar, who had built Dr. Sansum's home on the Samarkand Hills, submitted the winning bid for construction. Stockpiles of brick and lumber and structural steel began appearing at 317 West Pueblo Street. The tentative cost of the building was set at $66,000. If all went well, the clinic would be ready for occupancy in January, 1930.

But all did not go well. The euphoric bubble burst on Tuesday morning, October 29. The Sansums were at breakfast, listening to the news and weather on station KFI Los Angeles, when a newscaster interrupted with a stunning flash bulletin:

> ". . . pandemonium has broken out on the trading floor of the New York Stock Exchange . . . millions of shares are changing hands, unprecedented in Wall Street history . . . tickers running hours late . . . unrestricted short selling, investors panicky as brokers call in margin . . . investors reported leaping from skyscraper windows in Manhattan's financial district. . . ."

Dr. Sansum's scalp prickled with premonitory alarm. He grabbed the telephone to call his stock broker. The line was busy. It would remain busy throughout the rest of this nightmarish day.

"Mother," he said, "I'm scared. This doesn't sound like an ordinary fluctuation in the market to me."

The radio news bulletins became more frequent, more alarming as the morning of Black Tuesday wore on. When the Big Board closed at noon Santa Barbara time, an unprecedented 16,000,000 shares had changed hands. Prices were plummeting too fast for the ticker to keep up.

It was typical of Dr. Sansum that he seemed oblivious to the fact that in a few hours most of his personal investments had been wiped out. His first concern was for the future of his diabetes research program which was dependent on contributions from the private sector, doubly so now that the Carnegie Corporation had terminated its support. When hard times struck, the first casualty was always charitable contributions.

In great anxiety, Dr. Sansum left the clinic early that afternoon and drove over to Montecito to consult his friend and benefactor, George Owen Knapp, one of the country's wealthiest industrial magnates, a conservative and knowledgeable man of finance. He found the baron of "Arcady," the Knapp estate, out strolling in his formal gardens. Knapp's paper losses that day had been enormous compared to Sansum's.

"This drop in the market today has me worried sick, George," Dr. Sansum burst out. "Do you think I should cancel my plans for building the new clinic before I'm over-extended? I still haven't paid off my indebtedness on the Tallant Road place, you know."

Knapp waved him off. "The stock market ebbs and flows, Doctor. Always has and always will. This is a temporary slump. The country's economy will bounce back. Unemployment will taper off. The world is at peace. Business will stabilize. No, Father Sansum — by all means carry through on your plans to build your own clinic. This market collapse won't last, take my word for it."

Thus reassured by one of the top brains in the business world, Sansum made irrevocable commitments to his contractor to insure the Sansum Clinic's being built. But Sansum was to learn, at the bitter cost of his own personal fortune, that George Owen Kanpp's judgement was not infallible, that his crystal ball was clouded.

By the end of 1929, stocks had declined in value by an unbelievable fifteen *billion* dollars in just nine weeks. The curve showed no sign of bottoming out. In coming months, stock losses would total a mind-boggling $50,000,000,000. Santa Barbara, the nation, and the world, were facing the worst depression in history as New Year's Day 1930 dawned.

Into these troubled fiscal waters the Sansum Medical Clinic was launched with a hope and a prayer.

11

Tragedy Strikes
at Casa del Mar

For Dr. Sansum, the year he turned fifty — 1930 — seemed endless. As economic conditions continued their nose dive, it became necessary to apply for a bank loan to ensure completion of the $66,000 clinic.

William Gunterman, manager of the Santa Barbara branch of the Los Angeles - First National Trust and Savings Bank, listened attentively as Sansum outlined his dreams for a new Clinic, the paralyzing effect of the market crash on his personal fortune, the desperation he suffered when diabetic patients arrived for treatment with more and more of them pleading for credit to tide them over their own fiscal emergencies.

"A diabetic can't delay treatment until a depression is over," Dr. Sansum said. "And I simply cannot bring myself to reject a patient because he has no money. I never have, and God willing I never will. But I find myself at the end of my rope, Bill."

Gunterman, while well aware of the shaky

financial structure of the country as a whole, and fearing that conditions would worsen before they improved, believed that Dr. Sansum was a good risk, and approved the loan. But finding himself financially obligated to a banking institution was to take the fine edge off Dr. Sansum's peace of mind for many years to come, and, his family always believed, contributed to his eventual loss of health.

A two-story structure with full basement, the new Sansum Clinic was eye-pleasing in the clean lines of its Italian Renaissance style, with just enough ornamentation to relieve the austerity of its planes and to satisfy the aesthetic tastes of the Architectural Review Board which enforced local building ordinances.

Progress on the building seemed snail-slow, due to difficulties in obtaining materials, labor strife, and delays caused by more than the usual amount of inclement weather.

The new Clinic had over sixty spacious rooms. Hard times had not altered Dr. Sansum's original injunction to the architect to "keep it roomy." There were special provisions for oral surgery and eye, ear, nose and throat ailments, reflecting the fact that diabetes was no longer the sole thrust of the Clinic's research program. Classrooms were provided for Dr. Sansum's lectures, and for dietetic studies on the second floor. Laboratory facilities and the X-ray department were housed in the basement.

Construction was slated to be finished by year's end, but the general contractor kept advancing the date until it became obvious that the staff would not be able to move into their new quarters until the spring of 1931.

In the interim, Dr. Sansum became the victim of unexpected personal misfortune. On Sunday, the 25th of January, 1931, he was out at Isla Vista sheathing the roof of a new bedroom he was adding to Casa del Mar. While attempting to carry an unwieldy panel of plywood up a ladder, a wind gust caused him to lose his balance and fall a dozen feet to the ground, landing on his back.

Severely injured, Dr. Sansum was rushed to Cottage Hospital where orthopedic surgeon Rodney Atsatt gave him emergency treatment. X-rays confirmed his diagnosis of a compression fracture in the lumbar area of the spine. A damaged nerve to the ileum, the last division of the small intestine, caused paralytic ileus, a morbid condition which threatened serious complications.

For eight painful weeks Dr. Sansum languished impatiently in traction. Fortunately the intestinal paralysis cleared up early, and with total bed rest the spinal injury healed so that Dr. Atsatt was able to discharge his patient by March 24. Dr. Sansum emerged from his hospital confinement to find that his new Clinic building was at long last nearing completion. Crews were busy laying carpets, installing furniture and sophisticated laboratory equipment, while nurserymen busied themselves with exterior landscaping.

The staff which would inaugurate the new facility now numbered eleven physicians: Drs. Sansum, Gray and Hare, the original triumvirate; Dr. Hildahl I. Burtness; two husband and wife teams, Drs. Delbert and Doris McNamara and Drs. Leonard and Yolanda Brunie; two specialists recently arrived from the Mayo Clinic, Barkley S. Wyckoff, D.M.D., an oral surgeon, and John Childrey, M.D., an eye, ear, nose and throat specialist; and Alfred Koehler, M.D., a young internist who had served as Henry Ford's personal physician back in Detroit. He had special interests in endocrine research and would be Dr. Sansum's right-hand man in the research department. Rounding out full-time positions on the staff were Ruth Bowden, dietitian, John Sansum, maintenance superintendent, and Freeman Spinney, business manager.

The formal dedication of the new Sansum Medical Clinic was marked by a gala open house party on the evening of Saturday June 6. The Santa Barbara *Morning Press* covered the party as a major news event. Under bold headlines reading MEDICAL CENTER IS LAST WORD IN MODERNNESS, the *Press* reported:

"Dr. W. D. Sansum and his staff moved into a home of their own and held open house last night. More than one thousand persons, doctors, friends, patients and others interested in Dr. Sansum's work, attended the formal opening of the Sansum Clinic at 317 West Pueblo Street opposite the Cottage Hospital.

"The roomy corridors of the building were filled with people and a constant line filed into the spacious lobby. Persons from all walks of life looked over the new building and furnishings. Fine limousines, modest sedans, flashy sport cars and even a decrepit roadster or two were parked for blocks around the clinic.

"Beautiful flowers crowded every room. There were bouquets from doctors and friends in all parts of the United States, and many floral gifts from local people. The Sciots organization attended the opening in a body. The members presented Dr. Sansum with an attractive floral pyramid, the symbol of their organization . ."

The new clinic richly deserved the kudos it received from the media. It was equipped with large offices for the doctors on the staff, modern laboratories for clinical, metabolic and cardiac studies, and the surgical departments. Professional men recognized that the Clinic was particularly adapted to the examination and treatment of patients who would not require hospitalization. Not being intended as a hospital or sanitarium in any sense, patients requiring in-house care could be accommodated in the Cottage Hospital across the street.

"Certain types of cases can be adequately studied and treated in the clinic without the extra expense of hospitalization, which can run to ten or twelve dollars a day," a contemporary brochure stated. "Such patients provide themselves with room and board elsewhere. Rooms and apartments are readily available in the neighborhood of the Clinic. The Cottage Hospital maintains an out-patient dining room under the supervision of a dietitian, where patients on special diets may obtain meals without having to go downtown. There are also several dining rooms in the vicinity where special diets are served. Several of the hotels in Santa Barbara provide supervised dietetic service" — an indication that Santa Barbara was regaining its turn of the century status as the health center of Southern California.

It was basic to Dr. Sansum's professional credo that each patient be considered as an individual problem, requiring unique treatment. Before any medical service was offered, a thorough study was made, followed by physical examinations and necessary laboratory tests. Special examinations such as X-ray studies, electrocardiograms, basal metabolism tests and the like were available under the same roof if needed. Upon completion of these diagnostic examinations, each patient's findings were reviewed in a private conference between doctor and patient, at which times a detailed plan of treatment including medication, dietary instructions and other necessary advice was given.

Hospitalization was usually advised for diabetic

patients during the early part of their treatment, because of better facilities for adequate control, although many out-patients were cared for at the Clinic. Dr. Sansum was inflexible in one demand: absolute obedience to dietary management and any other specific instructions laid down by the patient's nurse.

"Instruction in self-management is a most important item of diabetic treatment under the Sansum system," he would always preface his health lectures to patients. "A comprehensive course has been formulated for diabetic patients where you will be taught how to test your own urine specimens for sugar. You will be required to know about food values, menu planning, and food substitutions. Those of you on insulin will be taught how to administer the drug so that you will be proficient at it when you return home, since regular insulin injections will be routine every day of your lives. Private and class instruction will be given on the second floor of the Clinic at 11:00 a.m. daily except Saturday and Sunday, and absenteeism will not be tolerated."

Upon their discharge from the Sansum Clinic, each patient was provided with follow-up report forms on which to record daily progress at home. At regular intervals, it was recommended that the patient return to the Clinic for a personal checkup.

Diabetics booked into Cottage Hospital were encouraged to look upon the hospital as a hotel, where they were free to come and go as they pleased, subject to only two restrictions: they must be in their rooms when the physician made his morning rounds, and again at mealtimes. It was obligatory to attend the general lectures and special classes. This last was sometimes difficult to enforce for patients in a reasonably good state of well-being, for Santa Barbara's lovely beaches and scenic hiking trails in the nearby foothill canyons were temptations difficult to resist, especially for persons from less-favored parts of the country.

However, on rare occasions Dr. Sansum was known to dismiss patients for failure to comply with his rules.

For years, lecture schedules at Sansum Clinic were as follows:

MONDAY — "Symptoms and factors in production of diabetes," by Dr. Sansum.

TUESDAY — "The treatment of diabetes — diet and insulin," by Dr. Alfred E. Koehler.

WEDNESDAY — "Dietary management — menu planning, substitutions, etc.," by Ruth Bowden.

THURSDAY — "Common complications of diabetes," by Dr. Doris McNamara.

FRIDAY — "Home management" by Dr. Hildahl I. Burtness.

Every other week, on Thursdays, Dr. Barkley Wyckoff lectured on "Focal infection" to explain to patients why they should have absessed teeth and tonsils removed to prevent the spread of infection to other parts of the body.

Two-week lecture courses were held on weekday afternoons at the Bissell Memorial Auditorium next door to the Potter Wing of the hospital. The first week's schedule was as follows:

MONDAY — "The value of various therapeutics in the treatment of diseases, rest, exercise, drugs, diet, surgery, X-rays," by Dr. Sansum.

TUESDAY — "Food requirements — necessary considerations in menu planning and food selection," by Ruth Bowden.

WEDNESDAY — "Elimination of wastes through the alimentary tract, kidneys, skin and lungs," by Dr. Burtness.

THURSDAY — "Digestion and indigestion," by Dr. Sansum.

FRIDAY — "Underweight, its causes and treatment," by Dr. Sansum.

The second week schedule was as follows:

MONDAY — "High blood pressure, clinical interpretation and treatment," by Dr. Sansum.

TUESDAY — "Degenerative heart disease, factors leading to the present increase," by Dr. McNamara.

WEDNESDAY — "A discussion of diseases caused by bacteria and sources of infection," by Dr. Sansum.

THURSDAY — "Glandular disturbances, a discussion of the glands of internal secretion in health and disease," by Dr. Koehler.

FRIDAY — "A discussion of causes, dangers, prevention and treatment of overweight," by Dr. Sansum.

During the 1930s, an ominous trend developed: the man on the street, hard pressed to survive in a time of economic depression, saw little excuse for "wasting" money on further diabetic research. Had not insulin solved that health problem for all time? Diabetics were now able to utilize sugar again; they no longer burned their own tissues to sustain life, as they had done before insulin. With their energy restored, they could resume normal living, except for the daily insulin injections. Why, then, keep on spending money on diabetes research?

But the diabetes battle was not yet won. Far from it. An alarming development began in the 1930s among diabetes patients who were middle aged when they had started on insulin ten years before. Prior to insulin, diabetics soon died. With insulin, they were surviving into a period of late middle life when diabetes-related complications frequently developed.

Physicians got their first inkling that the diabetes problem was renewing in a different form when patients who had survived their first decade of insulin therapy began complaining of unusual eye problems. Tiny red dots appeared on the retina — bulges in the walls of tiny veins, called microaneurysms. Before long the small veins leaked fluid, causing exudates or white spots, and bloody blotches spread across the retina.

Sooner or later a retinal vein would burst, flooding the eyeball with blood and causing instant blindness. Gradually, as this blood was absorbed, sight would return, only to be lost a few weeks later as other microscopic veins popped. Eventually the diabetes-caused blindness, known as retinopathy, became permanent, and was on its way toward becoming the leading cause of blindness in the United States.

This problem baffled Drs. Sansum, Koehler and Burtness, the Clinic's diabetes specialists. They knew that diabetic retinopathy did not occur in all diabetic patients, but once it did, it resisted treatment. Since it appears only in diabetics, Dr. Sansum and fellow researchers all over the world, in searching for the cause, suspected that high blood sugar might be the culprit. They attempted to find the perfect control for diabetes; patients were told to weigh each mouthful of food, to take precisely measured doses of insulin, and to check the urine several times daily for traces of sugar.

Bit by bit, results rolled in on this form of treatment. In Dr. Sansum's case, he did not live to learn the final verdict, which was that "control" was not the answer to diabetic retinopathy. Control helped certainly; the incidence of retinopathy with diet control was only 25 per cent, compared to 65 per cent in diabetics on a free diet. But records showed that very few patients were convinced that such a reduction in their chances of blindness was worth a lifetime of dietary deprivation, and elected to take their chances.

Dr. Sansum and fellow researchers had learned patience the hard way. Nothing came easy in the field of diabetes research; the disease had yielded its secrets reluctantly over a period of more than two thousand years, and the mid-1930's proved just as frustrating.

During the summer of 1932 the Sansum Clinic worked with the new "McCallum hormone," named after a Chicago physician who advanced the theory that the duodenum secreted a hormone which stimulated the pancreas's islands of Langerhans to secrete insulin. After receiving a small amount of the dried duodenal mucosa from Chicago, Dr. Sansum and his coworkers at the clinic were attempting to extract the McCallum hormone.

"If a careful microscopic study is made of the pancreas from patients who have died of diabetes," Dr. Sansum wrote in November 1932, "in some cases it is found that the islands of Langerhans have been completely destroyed. The complete destruction of the islands would of course account for diabetes because the gland could not manufacture insulin. However, in other instances we find that the islands of Langerhans appear perfectly normal, even though the patients died of diabetes. Such normal-appearing islands of Langerhans should have been able to secrete sufficient amounts of insulin to burn the patient's sugar. This is where Dr. McCallum's theory about a duodenal secretion enters the equation: he believes, and we in Santa Barbara are attempting to verify, that although in some cases a diabetic's islands of Langerhans are normal, they do not secrete insulin because of a lack of this duodenal secretory hormone."

Dr. Sansum realized that unraveling this enigma of medicine (which was to be proved in error) would probably take many years of laboratory experimentation. This did not dismay him or his fellow workers. Research, by its elemental nature, is a slow, plodding process, calling for infinite reserves of faith and patience. Dead-end streets, such as the search for oral insulin, could take years of time and money. But big breakthroughs, of which insulin, penicillin, and polio vaccine are examples, do not come along every day. They are the cumulative result of slow, agonizingly frustrating attention to detail, sometimes extending over the lifetimes of several persons. That is what medical research is all about, Dr. Sansum used to tell his associates; the essence of pure science.

With that knowledge always uppermost in his mind, Dr. Sansum kept doggedly at work as the great depression laid its paralyzing blight on their world, threatening to cut off at the source the very lifeblood of medical research — continuing financial support from the public at large, who in the last analysis were the beneficiaries who stood to gain the most from medical discoveries.

12

Weathering the 1930s Depression

Midway through 1932 it became obvious to Freeman Spinney, the Sansum Clinic's business manager, that the Clinic was on a collision course with bankruptcy if business didn't improve. Their next-door neighbor, the Cottage Hospital, had a growing census of empty beds and was experiencing financial crises with numbing regularity. Gone forever, it would appear, were the golden days when multimillionaires waited in the wings with wide-open purses eager to finance new construction or subsidize long-range research programs as a meritorious tax write-off device.

For Dr. Sansum, the early depression years were doubly stressful because his elaborate new clinic facility, erected with borrowed money, would revert to the bank if he could not keep up his payments. Immediate belt-tightening became essential to survival.

At the outset of the decade Dr. Sansum had been paying the top physicians on his staff a salary of $500 a month, a munificent wage by 1930 standards. But even this payroll had to be reduced and drastically, Spinney warned.

Dr. Sansum called an emergency staff meeting early in 1933 to break the bad news.

"If the clinic is to remain open during this period of economic unrest, each one of us must accept a cut in salary," he said. "You are all welcome to stay; but I regret to inform you that where more than one member of a family is on our payroll, it will become necessary to let one member go. You have but to consult your own appointment books to know why this has to be done."

The Sansum Clinic had two married couples on its medical staff, the McNamaras and the Brunies. Mrs. McNamara started the exodus by withdrawing in favor of her husband, Delbert. The Brunies resigned, moving to Pasadena where they opened a private practice. Dr. Hare, long Dr. Sansum's good right arm and personal advisor, departed for Washington D. C. to become superintendent of a large sanitarium at Takoma Park, Maryland.

The first salary cuts trimmed $50 a month from paychecks. Before the year 1933 was out, salaries had dropped to $400 and would fall to $350 by 1934. Everyone was equally affected by Dr. Sansum's new austerity program, including himself and his brother John who functioned as the general factotum around the plant. Even in spite of the pay cuts and other economies in all departments, manager Spinney was often hard put to scrape up money enough from income to meet his payrolls. During these trying times, Dr. Burtness served as assistant chief of staff.

The patient census dropped to such a low ebb in 1933 that Dr. Sansum, addressing a medical group in Los Angeles, theorized that diabetes seemed to flourish in good times while the frequency of new cases dropped sharply in lean times.

THE ORIGINAL SANSUM CLINIC, 1932
located at 317 West Pueblo Street opposite Cottage Hospital, boasted 60 spacious rooms. It was expanded in the 1950's, one casualty of the new floor plan being the famous lobby [shown below]. The site is now a parking lot for the new Sansum Clinic flanking Castillo Street, which was dedicated in 1977.

THE SANSUM BROTHERS' OFFICES

In the upper picture Dr. Sansum is shown in his Clinic office checking over menu sheets. The door to this office was always open to patients and staff. In charge of general management of the building and grounds was the doctor's younger brother John, shown in the maintenance office below.

EARLY SANSUM CLINIC DOCTORS
included, top left, Percival A. Gray, M.D.; Alfred E. Koehler, M.D., first Sansum
Foundation president; and lower picture, from left, Doris McNamara, M.D., Delbert
McNamara, M.D., and their son James, who grew up to be a physician and member of
the board of the Sansum Medical Research Foundation.

149

NEWLYWEDS AT SAMARKAND
Dr. Sansum's son Donald married Virginia Marie Benson of Santa Barbara in ceremonies at the Samarkand Hotel gardens on March 9, 1934. The scene is one block from the Sansum home.

DR. SANSUM'S PRIDE AND JOY
were his grandsons, born to Donald and Virginia Sansum. Upper picture shows the
proud grandparents with the firstborn, Armand, whose sex the doctor attempted to
predict, unsuccessfully. Eventually the Sansums had a trio of grandchildren [below].
Left to right, Armand, born 1934; William David, 1936; and Stephen, 1943.

151

TIME OUT FOR TRAVEL
Dr. Sansum was usually too busy to take pleasure trips, but an exception was a 1935 Hawaiian holiday [above]. Below, he and his wife Mabel [directly beneath chandelier] pose in Vienna's Schönbrunn Palace during their 1937 tour of Europe and Russia with a party of Canadian and American doctors.

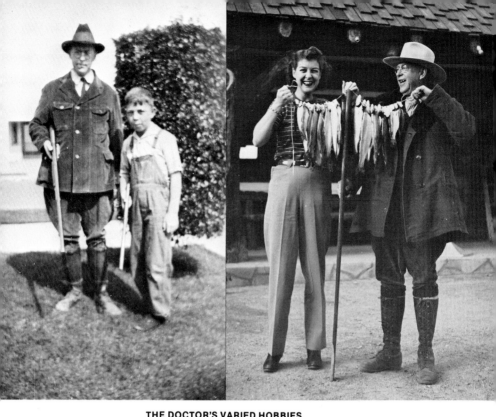

THE DOCTOR'S VARIED HOBBIES
included hunting [with son Donald], trout fishing, knitting ["Sansum Special" sweaters were coveted by Santa Barbara's leading citizens], and dogs of numerous breeds.

153

THE ENVIRONS OF SANSUM CLINIC

as they appeared in 1960. West Pueblo Street in foreground, Castillo on left, Bath on right. [1] shows the original Sansum Clinic Building of 1931 with mid-1950's additions. Cottage Hospital complex [since replaced] in center. [2] marks site of present Clinic of original hospital of 1890. [5] is the Masin Cytology Medical Group Inc., affiliated with the Sansum Foundation in research. [6] is the Knapp College of Nursing. [7] is the old Nuzum building. [8] marks the site of the laboratory facility of the Sansum

154

DR. SANSUM AND FRIENDS
Upper left, at the fountain which once stood in front of the Clinic the doctor poses with June Blakley [Baker], his chief nurse; upper right, with druggist friend and fishing crony Bob Sencerbox, his partner in the "vitamin project." Below, a young Hildahl Burtness, internist and Dr. Sansum's protege, beside the Model T Ford which brought him from Chicago to Santa Barbara in 1929.

DR. SANSUM'S FAVORITE RECREATIONS
included duties as a barbecue chef for Clinic staff parties staged at his beach house, Casa del Mar in Isla Vista, and fishing in the High Sierra streams and lakes. In bottom picture Dr. Sansum joins his Clinic business manager, Freeman Spinney, center, and "Dr. Burt" Burtness at Keough's mountain lodge at McGee Creek, Mono County.

LAST DAYS OF THE POTTER WING

The front veranda of the Potter Wing of Cottage Hospital was enclosed for office space in 1930 when Dr. Sansum founded his own private clinic. Below, a bulldozer starts demolition of the historic building where America's first insulin was produced, to make way for new construction in 1971.

157

DR. SANSUM'S LAST PHOTOGRAPH
was this one, taken at a Clinic Christmas party shortly before his sudden death from a cerebral hemmorhage on January 5, 1948, at age 67 His grave is marked by a simple tablet of gray granite [below] in the Sansum family plot at the seaside Santa Barbara Cemetery.

THANK YOU FOR A NEW LABORATORY
On June 9, 1966, the new Harry and Velma Morrison Laboratory building was donated to the Sansum Foundation. Mayor E. Don MacGillivray, right, presented a plaque of appreciation from the city to the Morrisons, while their long-time family doctor, H. I. Burtness, looked on.

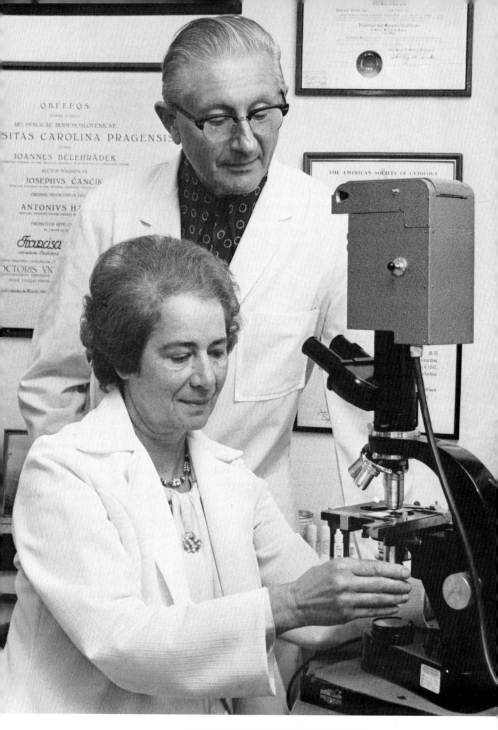

DRS. MARIANNE AND FRANCIS MASIN
Czechoslovakian scientists of world renown, joined the Sansum Medical Research Foundation in 1962, specializing in the early detection of cancer. At their own cytology laboratories the Drs. Masin are studying the detection of bladder cancer by examination of the urinary sediment [a "Pap smear" of the urine] and are adapting the flourescent staining technique which they pioneered to automated screening of cancer cells in a collaborative effort with Dr. John Frost and Johns Hopkins University.

160

DR. DONALD E. McMILLAN
is the director of diabetes research for the Sansum Foundation, and has won worldwide acclaim for his study of blood viscosity in diabetics and its relationship to the incidence of retinitis and nephritis in later life. In 1977 Dr. McMillan presented two papers on his findings before the 9th Congress of the International Diabetes Federation meetings in New Delhi and Madras, India.

161

TOP-RANKING FOUNDATION OFFICERS
include Casimir Domz, M.D., former director of diabetic research, current president of the non-profit Sansum Medical Research Foundation, and below, chairman of the board Hildahl I. Burtness, M.D., the last of Dr. Sansum's "old guard" at the original Clinic. Both are staff physicians at the modern Sansum Clinic.

163

MRS. VELMA MORRISON,
widow of building tycoon Harry Morrison of Boise, Idaho, who is actively interested in supporting ongoing research at Sansum and, with her husband, furnished half the funding for the laboratory.

FIFTY-FOUR YEARS LATER,
laboratory chemist Loyal C. Maxwell, Ph.D., left, and Carl Klass, third recipient of
insulin in 1922 join in 1976 with Dr. Donald E. McMillan, center, director of diabetes
research, in dedicating a plaque honoring the achievements of Dr. Sansum and his
chief chemist, Norman R. Blatherwick. Lower picture, a view of the main research
laboratory.

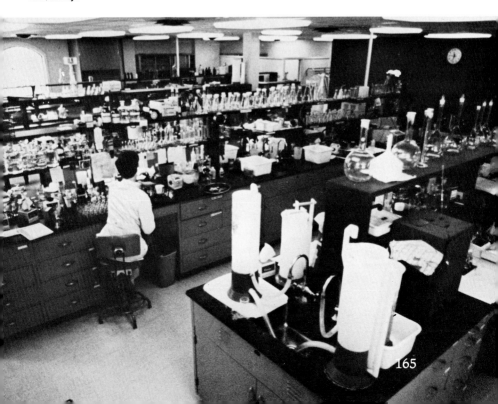

165

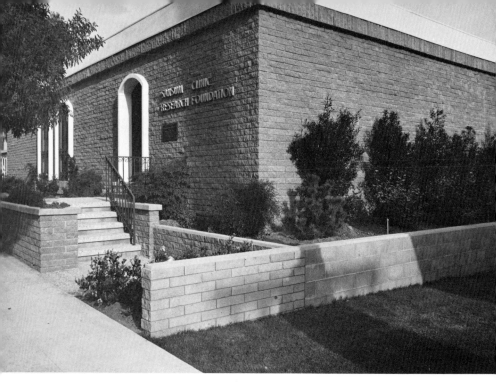

WHERE THE QUEST CONTINUES

against diabetes, arthritis, cancer and other diseases: the Sansum Medical Foundation's existing research laboratory at 2219 Bath Street. Illustration below shows how the facility will look when new floors are added to make room for the expanded research program now in the planning stages. The added space is dependent upon continued public support since governmental funds are not available for such a project.

"I believe this is because people eat more sensibly during economic adversity when all they can afford are the staple foods," Dr. Sansum explained. "I believe history will confirm that feasting induces diabetes while famine diminishes its incidence."

Patients' visits dropped so low that staff physicians were urged to take sabbatical leaves at reduced pay. The clinic's heart specialist, Dr. Delbert McNamara, a devout Seventh Day Adventist, decided that entering his church's overseas medical missionary program might be his answer to the depression. In order to qualify to practice medicine as a foreign missionary anywhere in the British empire, it became necessary for him to visit Edinburgh, Scotland, for brush-up studies preparatory to taking the stiff examinations imposed by the British Medical Board.

"I breezed through their written examination," Dr. McNamara wrote to his wife in Santa Barbara, "but the oral test was a humdinger. When the examiners started asking me questions about diabetes, I was so obviously better informed than they were that they quickly changed their line of questioning to tropical diseases, where I didn't fare so well. They told me later that they knew that any one on the staff of Santa Barbara's Sansum Clinic would outshine them where diabetes was concerned, so they just gave me an A-plus score on the diabetes section."

Although Dr. McNamara received official accreditation to practice on British soil anywhere in the world, his Adventist missionary work never materialized, due in part to being called up by the U.S. Navy Reserve several months before the United States entered World War II.

Dr. Sansum's low fee scales contributed to his own drop in personal income. As Dr. Barkley Wyckoff said, "Father Sansum's fees were always ridiculously low, even in the best of times. He never turned away a patient for lack of funds, and during the pit of the depression, he gave away his services at a rate you would find difficult to believe."

Dr. Sansum's son Donald graduated from Santa Barbara High School in 1933. It was the father's dream that Donald go to medical school and someday take over the operation of Sansum Clinic. But Donald had no interest in preparing for a medical career, enrolling instead in the Santa Barbara State Teachers' College.

"Virginia Marie Benson and I were married on March 9, 1934," Donald said. "Dad offered to pay both our living expenses if I would enroll at the University of Wisconsin, as the first step toward following his footsteps into Rush Medical College in Chicago. But we turned down his generous offer. My aptitudes lay in ranching and retail business. I guess that was a bitter disappointment to Dad, but he never tried to force me into changing careers."

As business declined at the Clinic and his financial difficulties continued to mount in the face of universal hard times, Dr. Sansum turned more and more to recreational activities. One of his favorite pastimes was giving backyard barbecues for the Clinic staff at his beach house in Isla Vista.

A state senator from Mono County, Jerry Keough, was one of Dr. Sansum's early diabetes patients. The senator owned a large resort lodge at McGee Creek in the High Sierra, where sportsmen paid two dollars for a night's lodging, half a dollar for a huge breakfast, and one dollar for a sumptuous supper. Out of gratitude to Dr. Sansum for saving his life, Senator Keough made the McGee Creek lodge available to him and his friends at any time. Several times a year Dr. Sansum took advantage of this invitation, often taking with him his business manager, Freeman Spinney; his assistant chief of staff, "Burt" Burtness; and a fishing crony who ran a pharmacy in Santa Barbara, Bob Sencerbox.

"Dr. Sansum was the most infinitely patient man I ever knew," Sencerbox recalls. "For example: when he snarled his fishline into an impossible tangle, where the rest of us would have cut it loose and thrown it away, Father Sansum would sometimes spend two or three hours laboriously untangling the line. And on days when the fish weren't biting, he would fish from dawn to dusk regardless. I never knew his equal for patience."

Dr. Sansum's favorite fishing hole was at June Lake in Inyo National Forest, too remote to visit regularly, whereas relaxation at Casa del Mar was only twenty minutes away. Since his cigar smoking and monthly poker sessions were frowned on at home, Casa del Mar became a welcome refuge for him.

During a storm in May 1934, Casa del Mar caught fire when rain leaked into a meter box and caused a short circuit. Because of its isolated location the fire was not discovered in time and the house burned to its foundations.

The loss stunned Dr. Sansum; his Isla Vista hideaway had become an essential part of his well-being. But the black cloud turned out to be lined with silver; he had insured the beach shack in 1926 at inflated values. Now, with the dollar worth so much more in purchasing power, the insurance would more than cover the rebuilding of Casa del Mar on a larger scale than the original.

This house-building project, Dr. Sansum later told his friends, literally saved his sanity during the darkest hours of the depression when he had difficulty paying his staff and meeting his mortgage payments on the Clinic.

The new House of the Sea had three bedrooms, yellow-painted board-and-batten siding, and a cedar shake roof. He was especially proud of the lavastone fireplace in the living room, since Mrs. Sansum did not permit fires in the hearth at the Tallant Road house because it increased her housecleaning tasks. The living room at Casa del Mar had picture windows opening on gorgeous views of the Pacific and the Channel Islands of Santa Cruz and Santa Rosa which lay like basking whales on the horizon, thirty miles away.

Through the years Dr. Sansum corresponded with many of his patients on a regular basis, especially his first insulin recipient, Charles Cowan, and his first juvenile case, Carl Klass. Writing to the latter on September 18, 1935, Dr. Sansum said:

> "I have been having a lot of fun this summer rebuilding our beach cottage . . . I have built a sort of Spanish type house with three bedrooms, bath, dining room and kitchen, and a beamed-ceiling living room twenty by thirty feet with a fireplace made of volcanic rock. The house surrounds a patio with a porch across the end. I have ceiled all of Casa del Mar with knotty pine which I have finished either with varnish or wax rubbed to a high gloss. I have worked out there practically every Saturday afternoon and Sunday throughout this entire summer."

No matter how hard times got, one thing Dr. Sansum refused to curtail was his continuing quest to conquer diabetes through research. With no more help coming from the Carnegie Foundation, and with most of his wealthy friends having financial difficulties of their own, Dr. Sansum was nevertheless able to solicit enough money to pay his staff and keep his laboratory experimental programs continuing without interruption.

"If there was any one thing in which Father Sansum was really accomplished, it was the art of fund raising,"

Dr. Wyckoff remembers. "And one of his most effective innovations was what he called his Birthday Research Plan."

A printed brochure which was given to every "graduating" diabetes patient explained the Birthday Research Plan as follows:

"The advances made in medicine as a result of medical research are gratifying alike to medical workers and the laity. However, there are many conditions concerning the cause and treatment of which we have only fragmentary knowledge. National recognition has been accorded the work done under Dr. Sansum's direction in the treatment of diabetes. The staff of the Sansum Clinic is now engaged in the study of problems connected with various other metabolic disturbances in addition to diabetes.

"During the last few years of the depression, income from former sources for the maintenance of this work has been materially reduced. To help maintain its research work, The Sansum Clinic is initiating a simple plan which has been so successful that it will be continued. The plan is that friends and patients who have been aided by the results of medical research contribute one dollar on each birthday anniversary to our research fund. Though seemingly modest in amount, such contributions assist in keeping our active research in progress and allow each person an opportunity to help."

It was customary for Dr. Sansum to send a personal Christmas card every year to former diabetic patients. It included a message which read, "Without a reasonable degree of health we cannot enjoy life. Yet how many of us give a thought to this priceless possession until it is perhaps too late to save it? In the past fifty years the average life expectancy of Americans has increased sixteen years, so much have we profited by the work of such researchers as Pasteur, Koch and Lister on the nature of infection and immunity, by the discoveries of specific remedies for yellow fever, syphilis, malaria, diabetes and pernicious anemia, by the development of the X-ray which makes early diagnosis possible, and particularly by the work done on infant feeding, which has perhaps been the chief factor in raising man's life expectancy.

There are thousands of problems yet to be solved, the solution of which would not only save the lives of thousands of individuals yearly, but would add to the enjoyment of living for millions. For work on these problems we need money — to pay for chemists, laboratories, and equipment. We cannot, in these times, expect a few men to carry the entire burden of expense.

"So I am suggesting that everyone whose life has been saved, or whose health has been improved, through the fruits of medical research, make a birthday gift of one dollar each year to this cause. Even if only a minor percentage of those in the United States who are indebted to medical research could be reached and would contribute one dollar per year, this would, I believe, exceed all money spent at the present time for this purpose. I hope that this plan meets with your approval, and that you will interest your friends in it also."

To the utter amazement of business manager Spinney, who had confessed to some cynicism that such an appeal would have any loosening effect on purse strings during bad times, envelopes began arriving at Sansum Clinic by the score, and eventually by the hundreds, each containing currency or checks, usually for higher amounts than the suggested one dollar.

Thanks to such a simple idea as the Birthday Research Plan, there was never any cessation of diabetes research at the Sansum Clinic during Dr. Sansum's lifetime.

On November 24, 1934, when everyone was in an expansive post-Thanksgiving mood, Dr. and Mrs. Sansum welcomed their first grandchild. During the latter stages of his daughter-in-law Virginia's first pregnancy, Dr. Sansum had boasted to the prospective father that as a trained disciple of Hippocrates, Dr. Sansum had the expertise to accurately foretell the sex of the unborn infant through certain vague but scientifically infallible signs.

Son Donald was skeptical, but to humor his father, agreed on a wager: Donald said he would sire a boy, Dr. Sansum asserted smugly that the baby would be female. The self-styled obstetrical prophet paid his bet promptly the day his grandson arrived and was christened Armand Berry Sansum.

"A rare failure in the system," Dr. Sansum brushed off his error. "The same bet will apply to your next offspring ?"

During Virginia Sansum's next pregnancy, Dr. Sansum confidently predicted another girl. William David Sansum II was born March 18, 1936. Again Dr. Sansum paid off. When Virginia became pregnant a third time — this was in 1943 — Dr. Sansum hedged somewhat, perhaps having lost faith in his prognosticative powers. Without making a cash bet, but feeling that the law of averages had now swung in his favor, Dr. Sansum again predicted a grand-daughter. Stephen

Dexter Sansum was born two days after Christmas.

Strike three! Dr. Sansum sheepishly dropped his pretentions to being a sex predictor. As things turned out, Stephen was the last Sansum grandchild, anyway.

In late July of 1936 Dr. Sansum issued a widely-reprinted report to his patients summing up the current status of the art of diabetes research. He wrote:

"The problem of diabetes is a very complex one. We have identified five types of diabetes:

(1) a deficiency in the insulin-making islands of Langerhans in the pancreas;

(2) a deficiency in the hormones of the pituitary gland, which secretes a hormone that stimulates the pancreas to function;

(3) a deficiency of liver function. The liver probably makes the hormone amylase, which is intimately related with insulin in changing glucose to glycogen.

(4) An over-active adrenal gland.

(5) An over-active thyroid gland.

"All five of these types of diabetes will eventually have a separate form of treatment, although of course insulin is specific for them all. The adequate use of insulin, together with a proper low-fat, high-carbohydrate diet, actually rests the pancreas, enabling it to make more of its own insulin. In the same group of cases over a ten-year period, the insulin requirements have dropped from an average of 76 units to less than 40 units per day, and thirteen per cent of the patients in this group are now making enough of their own insulin so that they do not have to take additional insulin hypodermically."

The Sansum Clinic became the "in" place for stars of the stage and screen to have the periodic check-ups necessary to cope with the stresses of Hollywood life.

"Usually the big stars would sign in anonymously and the Cottage Hospital staff always cooperated in keeping the curious away," recalls Dr. H. I. Burtness. "Harold Lloyd, John and Lionel Barrymore, Zeppo and Groucho Marx, Jimmy Cagney and his family, Ethel Barrymore and Gloria Swanson — these were typical celebrity names treated at Sansum."

In the summer of 1937 Dr. Sansum took his nose from the grindstone long enough to join a party of forty-five doctors, their wives and friends, making a total of eighty-six persons, on a tour of the Continent, Scandinavia, and Russia. The delegation was known as the Interstate Postgraduate Medical Association of North America and included doctors from Canada as well as the U.S.

In Moscow the group was checking into the Metropole Hotel on Red Square when they heard a burst of gunfire from the direction of the Kremlin walls. "Mrs. Sansum asked me what the noise was," Dr. Sansum later told friends in Santa Barbara. "It was Stalin purging himself of some Russian generals he believed were plotting to assassinate him. I could see the bodies of the slain men lying on the cobblestone pavement of Red Square but I told Mabel it was fireworks celebrating some kind of Red holiday."

On the USS *Manhattan* returning from the

European junket, Dr. Sansum struck up a lively acquaintance with Alfred E. Smith, ex-mayor of New York and erstwhile candidate for president. Back in Southern California, Dr. Sansum was in heavy demand that fall and winter as an after-dinner speaker, with audiences showing particular interest in the deplorable conditions of Russian hospitals, Soviet farm cooperatives and the pitiable state of the common peasants.

Inevitable changes eroded the original staff of the Sansum Clinic as the years went by. Dr. Percival Allen Gray left to join the rival Santa Barbara Medical Clinic, where he remained until his death in 1971, specializing in diabetes cases.

In 1938 Dr. Barkley Wyckoff, head of the clinic's department of oral surgery and one of Dr. Sansum's favorite fishing partners, came to him to report that he had noted a "definite reluctance on the part of many Santa Barbara physicians" to refer accident cases to him, or patients needing complicated oral surgery presumably because of his affiliation with the Sansum Clinic. There simply wasn't enough dental surgery to support a separate department, he said.

Father Sansum agreed. He said without hesitation, "Bark, open your private practice with my blessing. I will not replace you here — in fact I will make you a present of all the equipment in the oral surgery department. And I will refer all the Clinic's oral surgery work to your office."

13

Dr. Sansum's Work with Vitamins

In addition to being the co-manufacturer of the first insulin made in the United States, Dr. W. D. Sansum was probably the first doctor on the west coast to package vitamins for use by his private patients at cost.

Supplementary vitamins for the diet were still a new concept in the 1930s, and public acceptance of vitamin products, especially during the depths of the depression, was slow in coming. In 1938 Sharpe & Doan Pharmaceutical Corporation brought out Vitamin B made from rice polishings, an extremely expensive source. The product was priced at $10 per bottle of 100 tablets, or a month's supply. However, it failed to sell. The public was not yet sold on the efficacy of vitamins, and the price seemed exhorbitant.

A Sharpe & Doan salesman offered to unload 100,000 Vitamin B tablets in bulk at a penny apiece, an offer which tempted Dr. Sansum immediately. He conferred with his fishing buddy, druggist Robert

Sencerbox, who operated the Mission Pharmacy at Alamar and Hollister Avenues on the edge of town. The two friends decided to form a business partnership and bottle and label the vitamins which they could sell to Sansum patients at $2 a bottle and still recover their labor and overhead costs. This was only one-fifth the manufacturer's list price for the product.

Every patient for whom Dr. Sansum prescribed the new Vitamin B pills reported beneficial results. The supply soon ran out and could not be replaced at a price the average patient could afford. The Merck Company came out with a synthetic Vitamin B, which Sansum and Sencerbox bought in bulk for $2,000. It was capsulated and sold at cost.

By this time all the major pharmaceutical houses were jumping aboard the vitamin bandwagon. The economy was improving and the public was accepting the product, thanks to saturation advertising. So far, only straight Vitamin B was available; Dr. Sansum's advanced dietary research convinced him that what was needed was a combination pill or capsule containing Vitamin B-1 complex fortified with C.

Thanks to the fact that Dr. Sansum was a friend of the chief of pharmacy for Armour & Company, the meat packers, from his years as a medical student in Chicago, he and Sencerbox were able to procure Vitamin B complex pills at wholesale, since it was manufactured by Armour & Company as a byproduct of liver extract at their slaughterhouses, the largest in the world. Sencerbox's Mission Pharmacy in Santa Barbara thus became the first drugstore in California to retail Vitamin B complex pills to the public.

The closing years of the depression decade saw Dr. Sansum taking an ever-increasing interest in spectator sports such as baseball and football. His favorite idol was the legendary football mentor Howard Jones of the University of Southern California, who ranked as one of the country's foremost collegiate coaches from 1925 through the 1940 season. Jones' gridiron rivalry with his contemporary Knute Rockne of Notre Dame has become part of the American football legend.

A football player himself in his Normal School days in Wisconsin, Dr. Sansum had been a lifelong fan of the Wisconsin Badgers, but after moving to California he reserved his most fervent rooting for the USC Trojans. It was, therefore, a great thrill for him one summer day in 1938 when Bob Sencerbox brought two burly visitors to his office at the Sansum Clinic and introduced them as Coach Howard Jones of USC and his assistant Jeff Cravath, the noted All-American center.

Dr. Sansum reacted with the awe and adoration of a teenager asking for an autograph from his favorite rock singer. He insisted on the famous pair remaining for a chat. Jones and Cravath were in town to speak before the Exchange Club at the Carrillo Hotel, and welcomed the chance to kill some time with such a fascinating conversationalist as Dr. Sansum.

"I sat in on the meeting," Sencerbox recalled. "You would have expected the discussion would have been about football, but it didn't turn out that way. Now that he had his heroes buttonholed in his office, Father Sansum couldn't resist the opportunity to expound on his favorite topic, health diets. He told Jones a lot about metabolism which the great coach didn't know, including the physiology of fatigue and what foods were best for athletes in times of intense emotional and physical stress. Jones told me later that he learned a lot from Father Sansum that day, including diet tips which he applied at the USC training table."

But one of Sansum's pet theories was rejected by Howard Jones. "The day of an important game,"

Sansum said, "such as with Notre Dame or UCLA, let your players sleep in — till ten o'clock if they want. It will pay dividends on the gridiron after the kick-off." So far as is known, the Trojan players did not get to sleep in on days when big games were scheduled.

Every December Dr. Sansum habitually sent in a mail order to reserve Rose Bowl tickets from the Tournament of Roses Association in Pasadena, for himself, son Donald, friend Sencerbox, and brother John Sansum.

Another boyhood trait which Dr. Sansum never outgrew — his love for the circus — had its echo in Santa Barbara. Ringling Brothers' Circus, later merged with Barnum & Bailey to form "the greatest show on earth," had wintered in his home town of Baraboo during his adolescent years. Whenever the circus came to Santa Barbara and pitched its big top on the Estero, a dry lake bed on the lower east side of town, John Ringling himself would come out to the Sansum Clinic to chew the rag with his boyhood friend Willie Sansum. Ringling always left half a dozen free passes on Sansum's desk, and they never went to waste.

Dr. Sansum was not a social "joiner." He held memberships in La Cumbre Lodge No. 642 of the Masons, as well as the Knights Templar and Sciots, but he rarely had time to attend lodge meetings. In the professional field he belonged to the California Society for the Promotion of Medical Research, the Society for Experimental Biology and Medicine, the American Medical Editors and Authors Association, the American Diabetes Association, the American and California Medical Associations, and the Association for the Study of Internal Secretions. He was also a fellow and life member of the American College of Physicians. Locally he had served as president of the Santa Barbara County Medical Association and as chief of staff of Cottage Hospital.

In an address delivered before the general session of the American Dietetic Association in Los Angeles, Dr. Sansum brought his audience up to date on advances being made in Santa Barbara to slow down the absorption of insulin so as to make a single injection last longer.

"Highly purified insulin was absorbed so rapidly that the effectiveness of a dose lasted only four or five hours," Dr. Sansum said. "It therefore became necessary to give at least three doses of insulin a day, one before each meal and in severe cases a fourth dose at bedtime, midnight or even at two o'clock in the morning. Children, especially, often needed a fourth dose.

"How could we slow down this absorption? The first outstanding demonstration that a glandular extract of the nature of insulin could be made to have a markedly augmented and prolonged action came in 1935 by Loyal C. Maxwell, Ph.D. He showed that the anterior pituitary sex hormone could be made ten times more effective by the addition of a minute amount of zinc. It was demonstrated that the increased effectiveness was due to slowed absorption, and it was soon proved that this principle could also be applied to insulin.

"Dr. Fritz Bischoff of the Cottage Hospital research department discovered that tannic acid slowed the absorption of insulin from four to six and even to twelve hours. For some months in 1935, as reported by Dr. Percy Gray, such a preparation of insulin tannate was used by us successfully in the treatment of diabetes. One dose of such insulin tannate, given in the evening, would last through the night and ensure a normal or even subnormal blood sugar in the morning. In 1936 Dr. Bischoff discovered that histone, an alkaline protein obtained from the thymus glands of calves, made an effective insoluble insulin compound that would last 24 hours or longer without the addition of zinc."*

The great advantage of slow-acting insulin was that it gave the diabetic patient a wider margin of safety between "the shakes," caused by low blood sugar, and coma, caused by high blood sugar.

Shortly after the discovery of slow-acting insulin, Dr. Maxwell went abroad to continue his long and distinguished career in the field of diabetes research, climaxed by his installation of the world's largest insulin manufactory in Buenos Aires, Argentina, which he managed until his retirement. He moved to San Clemente, California, in 1965.

The long years of financial worry, the making of daily rounds of hospital patients, the unceasing need to raise funds for research, were finally taking their physical toll on Dr. Sansum. In 1938 he yielded to Dr. Delbert McNamara's insistence that he submit to a complete physical examination. When all clinical tests had been completed and evaluated, the two men met in Dr. McNamara's office to go over EKG read-outs, X-ray films and blood test reports.

"Father Sansum," Dr. McNamara came straight to the point, "you are in the early stages of arteriosclerotic disease and high blood pressure. You've got to unload some of your work on your subordinates before you topple over with a CVA. In fact, my professional advice to you is that you retire from practice at once."

Dr. Sansum appeared startled by his colleague's pessimism.

"Retire, Mac? I'm not even sixty yet! It's unthinkable!"

"Not half as unthinkable as my having to serve

---

* A U.S. patent for Histone insulin was issued to Bischoff but it was never placed on the market due to its similarity to Protamine.

prematurely as one of your pallbearers," Dr. McNamara snapped. "Keep up this pace and you'll never *see* your sixtieth birthday."

Dr. Sansum ignored the advice . . .

In 1938 a wealthy Bostonian, William Bingham II, established a fund to provide free insulin for all of Dr. Sansum's juvenile diabetes patients whose parents were unable to afford the drug. Every month for ten years, until Mr. Bingham's death, a check was mailed to the Sansum Clinic secretary, Elizabeth Buell, to cover the children's insulin account at Cottage Hospital. In 1948 the fund was continued by Mrs. Sarah Fleischmann until her death on July 4, 1960.

The American Diabetes Association was organized in 1940 and held its first annual meeting in June, 1941, in Cleveland. Dr. Elliott P. Joslin, pioneer insulin researcher, was honorary president; the co-discoverers of insulin, Drs. Banting and Best, were vice presidents. Dr. W. D. Sansum of Santa Barbara was honored with an appointment to the charter council of the ADA, along with his old friend and mentor, Dr. Roland T. Woodyatt.

The following October, the U.S. Naval Reserve called Lt.j.g. Delbert McNamara to active duty. He happened to be visiting Santa Barbara on leave the first Sunday in December when the radio announced that the Japanese were attacking Pearl Harbor. With America at war, Dr. McNamara was soon on his way across the Pacific for his tryst with destiny at Guadalcanal and Guam, serving as a medical officer for the U.S. Marines.

1942, fated to be a pivotal year in Dr. Sansum's life, opened on a happy note; he was able to pay off the final installment on the mortgage he had placed on the Clinic in 1930. To celebrate his new freedom from debt, Dr. Sansum splurged and bought his wife an extravagant gift — a large Sarouk rug loomed in Persia.

The shooting war came much too close for comfort on the evening of February 23, 1942, less than three months after Pearl Harbor. The Sansums were at home, listening to President Franklin D. Roosevelt's Washington's Birthday "fireside chat" over radio KTMS, when thumps of distant cannonading rattled their window panes.

The gunfire came from the Japanese submarine I-17, which had surfaced at sunset off the coast directly in front of the Sansum beach cottage in Isla Vista. Cruising leisurely up the coast for another three miles, the crew of the sub's deck gun lobbed twenty-five high explosive five-inch shells ashore, but did no military damage. Historically it was the first time since the War of 1812 that shells fired in anger by an enemy had exploded on U.S. soil.

Within a few days Dr. Hildahl I. Burtness, Sansum's assistant chief of staff, took a leave of absence to enlist in the Navy. He was immediately assigned to the Pacific Theater of Operations as a medical officer, and wound up in the jungles of New Guinea.

With employes leaving almost every week to join the armed forces, Dr. Sansum found himself increasingly overworked. At that time he was under the personal care of Dr. Hugh Stephens, replacing the absent Dr. Burtness. In July 1942, Dr. Stephens ran a series of EKG tests on Dr. Sansum and was troubled by what he saw on the tapes. A serious heart attack was imminent unless Dr. Sansum stopped all physical activity and submitted to prolonged bed rest.

Dr. Sansum took one look at the electrocardiograms and knew his life depended on following his doctor's advice. The time had come to retire from active practice.

14

A Medical Research Foundation

The irrefutable warning of impending heart damage shown on the electrocardiograms drove Dr. Sansum into reluctant seclusion at his Isla Vista beach house. He disconnected the telephone and with his brother John attending him, spent six months at Casa del Mar. When his health had improved sufficiently for him to return to his home in town, Dr. Sansum announced that he was leaving active medical practise, but would continue his research.

"Father Sansum made an honest stab at retirement," Bark Wyckoff remembers. "For three whole days he joined the gaffers who sun themselves and whittle and play cribbage in Plaza del Mar, a city park still favored by the elderly. But it didn't work. Hell, before the week was out Father Sansum was back at the clinic, working on his long-term project concerning the effect of acid-ash diets on blood pressure. But he never made his hospital rounds of patients again."

A tragedy occurred in 1942 which saddened Dr. Sansum and the world of medicine. Its victim was Sir Frederick Banting, M.D., the discoverer of insulin in 1921. He had joined the Royal Canadian Air Force and was killed when his plane crashed on the desolate coast of Nova Scotia while flying a top secret military mission to London. Sugar, the substance which Banting had researched clinically throughout his career, was found gumming up the aircraft's fuel lines, proving that he had been slain by an enemy saboteur.

During 1943, in his second year away from active practice, Dr. Sansum and his chemists were able to make important reports on the use of citric acid to partially replace a deficiency of hydrochloric acid in the stomach, a common cause of indigestion.

Demonstrating the slow, steady progress inherent in research, Dr. Sansum had begun this study prior to 1929. Now he was able to demonstrate that for the same degree of acidity in the stomach, lemon juice was just as effective as nature's own hydrochloric acid. This was the acid which had stymied all efforts to perfect an oral insulin, since one drop of hydrochloric acid had the capacity to destroy 1,000 units of insulin in the digestive process.

"Lemon juice is more efficacious than grapefruit juice for this purpose," he reported. "The acidity of lemon juice, we have found, is sufficient to regulate the emptying time of the stomach, to destroy some of the harmful bacteria, and to aid in the liberation of calcium. We have found that two ounces of lemon juice with each meal seems to prevent indigestion, as well as being rich in Vitamins, especially Vitamin C."

On Sunday afternoon, April 16, 1944, Dr.

186

Sansum's brother John, assistant manager of the clinic, dropped dead of a heart attack at his home on Hollister Avenue. He was only 48. Heart disease was hereditary in the Sansum family; it had claimed both parents and would contribute to the deaths of his seven brothers and sisters, a fact which forced Dr. Sansum to reflect on his own mortality.

Severely jolted by John's death, Dr. Sansum belatedly ordered his attorney to draw up a will. While he knitted endless sweaters for friends, he pondered how his lifelong crusade against diabetes and diabetes-related diseases could be perpetuated in the event of his own death.

Out of these sober meditations was born the Sansum Clinic Research Foundation (the name was later changed to the Sansum Medical Research Foundation), which he organized in May 1944 under the laws of the State of California and the federal government as a non-profit organization to be maintained solely through tax-exempt donations from patients, friends, and the Sansum Clinic. Members of the Clinic would donate their time to the research work. Any and all donations to the Sansum Foundation were eligible for income tax deductions, at both state and federal levels.

The by-laws of the Sansum Foundation defined its purposes:

> 1. To encourage, foster, promote, further and to engage in scientific and educational research work of every kind and nature;
>
> 2. To exist and operate exclusively for the purposes set forth above;
>
> 3. To do and perform, without limitations, any and all things necessary, suitable and proper for, or incidental to, the accomplishment of

any of the purposes, or the attainment of any of the objects set forth above;

4. The corporation shall engage only in scientific and educational research work.

5. None of the income of the corporation shall inure to the personal benefit of any member thereof.

Three classes of membership were set up by Dr. Sansum — voting, sustaining, and honorary. Members of the staff of the Sansum Clinic were the voting members. Any person who contributed one dollar or more annually to the Foundation became a sustaining member. Honorary members would be elected by the board of trustees.

Dr. Alfred E. Koehler became the first president of the Sansum Medical Research Foundation, and carried on its initial research program, using Cottage Hospital laboratory facilities.

World War II ground inexorably toward its close. Hitler was knocked out in Europe in the spring of 1945 and the terminal phase of the conflict shifted to the Pacific as summer approached. Almost overlooked in the accelerating pace of the war was the death, on July 21, of Dr. Sansum's intimate friend and principal benefactor, George Owen Knapp. The grand old man of Cottage Hospital philanthropies died as a patient there, at the age of 90.

The atomic bomb hastened the surrender of Hirohito's forces in the Pacific early in August. By the beginning of 1946 the Sansum Clinic welcomed back its own special war heroes to private practice: Navy Commander Delbert H. McNamara, who had won a

Silver Star and Purple Heart for his heroism in the invasion of Guam, and Navy Commander Hildahl I. Burtness, who had served as a medical officer in New Guinea and in naval hospitals in San Diego and San Francisco.

Throughout 1946, Dr. Sansum doggedly curtailed his activities, confining himself to his blood pressure research on rats. He knitted sweaters, played poker at Casa del Mar, fished occasionally at low-altitude lakes and streams in the Sierra Nevada, put aside temptation to resume cigar smoking, and in general lived the restricted if impatient routine of a convalescing heart patient.

Although he was at least thirty years ahead of his time, Dr. Sansum in 1947 became intensely interested in a far-out idea — a method whereby cells of the living pancreas could be grown in test tubes to create an insulin-producing organism which could be transplanted surgically into the human liver. If successful, it would be a boon for diabetic patients. Complete organ transplants had been attempted previously, but ended in rejections.

The sensational concept, never before conceived by scientists, attracted the attention of Major Max C. Fleischmann, who in July 1947 informed Dr. Sansum that he would contribute $75,000 to the Sansum Medical Research Foundation, payable in five annual installments of $15,000, to research the feasibility of pancreatic transplants. The gift was predicated on Dr. Sansum being able to personally supervise the project for at least five years.

Work began at once to prepare a special laboratory in the old Potter Wing, under Dr. Sansum's watchful eye to assure its meeting his unique specifications. The process of growing animal tissues in test tubes was already being studied at Johns Hopkins University, so Cottage Hospital sent one of its research staff, Douglas

Warner, Ph.D., to Baltimore to study the Johns Hopkins techniques and report back to Santa Barbara.

"Success in this venture," Dr. Sansum told the news media, "would mean a significant advance in medical science's continuing efforts to deal with diabetes and other metabolic disorders. We will keep the press informed as progress develops."

The new transplant laboratory where Dr. Warner would be carrying out the test tube experiments with Dr. Sansum included a special "clean room," partly glass enclosed and lighted from the outside, which would be kept as totally sterile as was scientifically possible. Elaborate precautions and devices to maintain absolute sterility would be used, which added substantially to the $25,000 which Major Fleischmann poured into the laboratory during the year. One of the items was an artificial fog which would be injected into the clean room every morning. This vapor would condense into moisture on the ceiling, walls and furnishings, and automatically wash them. Scientists at Johns Hopkins pledged Dr. Sansum their full cooperation in the Santa Barbara project.

Dr. Sansum divided his time during the remainder of 1947 between his own laboratory experiments in pancreatin production and the effect of acid-ash diets on blood pressure, and in supervising the construction of the new Fleischmann transplant laboratory. It was expected that the pancreas experiments would get under way around the first of February, 1948.

After recuperating from USC's 49 to 0 drubbing at the hands of Michigan in the Rose Bowl game on New Year's Day, Dr. Sansum appeared in good spirits on Monday, January 5, 1948, when he spent the morning in his office dictating letters while he knitted on what he called a "June Lake sweater" for his friend Bark Wyckoff.

Dictation completed, Dr. Sansum went outside

shortly before noon, informing his co-worker Dr. Doris McNamara that he was going over to the hospital to check on the animals he was using in his blood pressure experiments.

Reaching his laboratory, Dr. Sansum entered a smaller side room where the rat cages were kept. His laboratory assistant, Elsie Hill, heard the sound of a heavy fall, followed by a feeble cry of "Help me — help me!"

Rushing to investigate, Miss Hill found Dr. Sansum crumpled on the floor below his workbench, where an overturned Bunsen burner spewed its torch toward a caged white rat which Dr. Sansum had been examining, the sphygmomanometer still attached to its body, tiny frightened sounds coming from the little animal.

"Get — Burt," Dr. Sansum gasped before he lapsed into unconsciousness, referring to his personal physician, Dr. Burtness.

Dr. Sansum was rushed upstairs to a private room, there being no intensive care unit at Cottage Hospital in those days. Doctors and nurses were summoned by emergency bells on all floors. The Sansum family was notified. Within moments the grim news had flashed throughout Cottage Hospital and the Sansum Clinic: beloved Father Sansum had suffered an apparent heart attack or stroke.

Two old friends, Drs. Burtness and Delbert McNamara, were at Dr. Sansum's bedside when vital signs ceased at 2:10 p.m. It fell to "Dr. Burt" to go into a nearby room to break the news to wife Mabel Sansum, son Donald, and sister Mary, who lived in Santa Barbara. There were two other sisters and a brother surviving in the midwest.

The cause of death was determined to have been a ruptured aneurysm of the pontine artery, deep inside the brain. Dr. Sansum's allotted time on earth measured out to 67 years, three months, and ten days.

He had died as he often said he would, with the harness on. His lifelong crusade against diabetes was unfinished, as he always expected would be the case. But there were other probing minds and talented hands to carry on where Dr. Sansum had left off, in the years ahead, just as he had picked up the torch dropped by Dr. Nathaniel Bowditch Potter twenty-eight years before . . .

15

Carrying On the Founder's Crusade

Dr. Sansum died believing he had left his personal and business affairs in good order, and that his successors would be able to carry on his work at the Sansum Clinic and the new Medical Research Foundation without interruption. But soon after his funeral, legal complications surfaced to plague his executors.

Dr. Sansum's last will and testament had been drawn on May 12, 1944, shortly after his brother John's sudden death. Filed for probate in the Santa Barbara County Superior Court on January 7, 1948, it named his widow Mabel Drew Sansum as principal beneficiary and executrix, with the Security-First National Bank of Los Angeles handling details of administration.

For reasons of delicate health, Mrs. Sansum waived her role in settling the estate, a function which was assigned to the Santa Barbara law firm of Heaney, Price, Postel & Parma. County appraiser George W. Edmonds set a valuation of $152,649.11 on the estate for tax purposes.

The first issue to be resolved was the future of the Sansum Clinic, over which internal friction was already developing. Mrs. Sansum had never been involved in her husband's business affairs, and their son Donald was deeply engrossed in his own enterprises.

It was known that Dr. Sansum wanted his business manager and long-time friend, Freeman P. Spinney, and his chief dietitian, Ruth Bowden, to have equal partnership in the Clinic, and they operated for the greater part of 1948 on that basis. Then the state attorney general reminded them that such an arrangement was not legal under the laws governing medical partnerships in California, which required that all partners had to possess medical degrees.

The staff sent Dr. Delbert McNamara to Sacramento to determine the proper reorganization of the Clinic. He returned with the word that Spinney and Miss Bowden, not having medical degrees, were not qualified to serve as full partners. Miss Bowden accepted the verdict and continued in her position as chief dietitian until her retirement in 1958, but Spinney angrily tendered his resignation in late 1948 and moved away from Santa Barbara.

This left two options open: either dissolve the Clinic as a corporate entity, or have the Sansum Estate sell it to the highest bidder. The existing staff would be the logical buyers, but raising the $250,000 which was the minimum amount the Sansum heirs were willing to accept for the property proved to be extremely difficult. The heirs also requested free medical care for the widow and Donald and Virginia Sansum during their lifetimes as part of the package.*

Through the heroic efforts of Dr. Delbert

---

* Mabel Drew Sansum suffered a series of minor strokes starting in late 1949 which rendered her a bedridden invalid until her death of a cerebral thrombosis at her home on Tallant Road on December 19,

McNamara and associates, the needed money was finally raised and the Sansum Medical Clinic was conveyed *in toto*, plant and good will, to a legal partnership composed of six medical doctors, H. I. Burtness, Alfred E. Koehler, Douglas F. McDowell, Delbert H. and Doris E. McNamara, and James H. Saint. Dr. Delbert McNamara was elected chairman, and Allan M. Duncan business manager to replace Spinney. Henceforth the Sansum Clinic had no connection with its founder except in name.

Dr. Sansum's legacy to medicine, his Medical Research Foundation, continued under the direction of Dr. Koehler, focusing mainly on winding up Dr. Sansum's studies on the roles that fat and cholesterol play in the degenerative diseases which claim the highest mortality in man. Koehler's attention was channeled to the chemistry of the disturbances that lead to blood vessel changes which are such a serious problem in uncontrolled diabetes and arteriosclerosis.

The $75,000 research project concerning the growth of pancreas cells in the laboratory for transplantation purposes in human diabetic patients, to have been financed by five annual grants from the Fleischmann Foundation, had to be cancelled. The gift had been contingent on both Sansum and Fleischmann remaining alive during the half decade covered by the grant. As events proved, neither man survived; Major Fleischmann contracted an inoperable carcenoma of the pancreas, the most difficult kind of cancer to diagnose, and died at his Carpinteria ranch on October 16, 1951. The special laboratory in the Potter Wing, in which

---

1957 at the age of 73. Dr. Burtness continued to provide free medical care for Mrs. Sansum until her death, as per the agreement at the time ownership of the Clinic was conveyed to the new partnership.

Major Fleischmann had already invested $25,000, was almost ready for opening at the time of Dr. Sansum's death. It was salvaged for other uses. Dr. Warner, who was to have carried on the transplantation project at Cottage, eventually established his own medical laboratory in Santa Barbara.

Research activities during the first five years following Dr. Sansum's death were continued by Dr. Koehler, but terminated when he suffered a disabling stroke in 1953 which led to his untimely death in 1958 at age 62. Dr. Burtness succeeded him as president of the Sansum Medical Research Foundation, serving until 1977 when he became chairman of the board.

For the remainder of 1953 and the entire year 1954, research activities at the Sansum Foundation were dormant. Then, in June 1955, Dr. Casimir A. Domz took over the reins and soon had revitalized the Foundation's activities.

Dr. Domz was a native of Detroit who had been educated at the Universities of Detroit and Michigan, interned at Queen's Hospital in Hawaii, then served two years at the Mayo Clinic before going into the U.S. Army for two years. He was a medical officer stationed at Camp Cooke (now Vandenberg Air Force Base) in northern Santa Barbara County at the time of his discharge.

Working part-time with the Foundation, Dr. Domz began his studies in the fields of gastrointestinal and stomach disorders, later switching to immunology. In the latter field he was successful in producing antibodies in tissue cultures which could kill viruses in the test tube.

The first successful transplantation of bone marrow for agammaglobulinemia was performed by Dr. Domz on a 55-year-old woman in 1959. He was named director of laboratories for Sansum Foundation, a post he held until being elevated to a vice-presidency in 1972, and the presidency in 1977.

Financing — the perennial bugaboo of research scientists — had been Dr. Sansum's special talent. But in 1960, twelve years after his death, Dr. Sansum's influence reached from beyond the grave to inject new life into his Foundation. One of his first diabetic patients at the old Potter Metabolic Clinic, prior to the discovery of insulin, had been a 24-year-old woman from Louisville, Doris Fay Palmer, the daughter of a wealthy Kentucky furniture manufacturer. Her prognosis was bleak when Dr. Sansum admitted her to the Potter Metabolic Clinic in 1921. When insulin became available in May 1922, she was one of the "first twenty" to receive injections, and her health improved as dramatically as in the Cowan and Klass cases described in earlier chapters.

Miss Palmer, who never married, was living in Santa Barbara when she inherited her father's substantial fortune. She died of a coronary thrombosis on August 5, 1960, at the age of 63.

In gratitude for, and in recognition of Dr. Sansum's legacy to her of 39 extra years of relatively good health, Doris Fay Palmer bequeathed to the Sansum Medical Research Foundation a self-liquidating trust, restricted to diabetes research only, providing up to $50,000 a year, to terminate as required by law, in 1980.

Two primary research studies in diabetes inaugurated by the new Doris Palmer Diabetes Research Fund were under the supervision of Dr. Domz. The first study, implemented by Matthew C. Urbin, Ph.D., was concerned with antagonists to insulin in the blood, which prevented insulin from performing its task. A new school of thought had developed the concept that diabetes mellitus was not due solely to lack of insulin, but rather its lack in a form necessary for lowering blood glucose. Knowledge as to the natures of the complexes of insulin and its antagonists was sparse.

Whether they were involved in the vascular complications of diabetes was the question researchers hoped to answer.

Laboratory procedures of a refined and complex nature were set up, designed to increase knowledge of antagonism to insulin by other circulatory molecules. The study involved isolation of insulin complexes from the serum of diabetic hamsters by the methods of ion exchange resins and disc electrophoresis. Comparisons of these complexes were made with those isolated from human sources, in an effort to clarify their physiochemical nature. The Sansum Foundation also directed investigations of ILA (insulin-like activity) by means of the rat diaphragm technique, in hopes of pinpointing some of the factors involved in the uptake of glucose in living tissues.

The second basic undertaking in the Foundation's earliest research funded by the Palmer Trust had to do with the permeability of cells to simple sugars, or monosaccharides. One of these, glucose, depended on insulin for transfer across cellular membrances, though virtually nothing was known about the fundamental mechanisms of these processes. Experiments got under way to elucidate the mechanism of monosaccharide transfer in the hope that it would result in better understanding and control of diabetes.

Dr. Sansum's long-standing ambition had been to expand the work of his Research Foundation into other fields than diabetes, notably cancer, arthritis, and heart disease, but it had been prevented by lack of adequate funding. In the early 1960s gifts totaling over $71,000 for cancer research were received from the American Cancer Society and the Damon Runyon Cancer Fund, for projects carried on by two cytologists, Francis and Marianna Masin, graduates of Charles University, Prague, Czechoslovakia, who joined the Sansum Research Foundation staff in 1962. Appropriately

198

enough, in July 1962 they established their cytology laboratory in the very same laboratory where Dr. Sansum had labored and in which he had suffered his fatal stroke.

The Drs. Masin's credentials were of the highest order, testifying to outstanding accomplishments in cancer research in Europe, South America, and more recently at the Hospital of the Good Samaritan in Los Angeles, where they had been first interviewed by Dr. Domz. He placed them in charge of cytology research to study the malignant transformation of cells. "Santa Barbara," Dr. Domz said, "is lucky to get the Masins."

"The ultimate goal of cancer research has always been to discover the cause, and then to prevent the disease," the Masins said. "However, as clinical cytologists we must put our greatest emphasis at this time on the *early detection* of cancer. Hence, the main target of our current studies is the development of practical diagnostic techniques."

It was found that not all cells of the body were equally susceptible to malignant growth. Frequently, cells become cancerous in organs which show a considerable rate of cell division, such as bone marrow. From areas where malignancies are triggered off, the abnormal cells can be collected and identified. Their detection thus forms the basis for cytologic diagnosis of cancer — the specialty which the Drs. Masin brought to Sansum.

Cancer of the cervix has become a preventable disease, Foundation researchers report. There are still difficulties, however, in classification of the types of abnormality found in cells of the cervix. The purpose of studies conducted at the Sansum Foundation by the Drs. Masin is to work out methods which would make possible a clear distinction between truly malignant cells, and those which only look malignant.

Another field of intensive endeavor of the Masins is

a study of the relationship between smog, cigaret smoking and other air pollutants to lung cancer, the leading cancer killer in America today. The Masins obtain sputum specimens from smokers periodically which disclose that in some individuals, progressive alterations in the variety of pulmonary cells affected by carcinogens and other components of cigaret smoke have occurred. The dynamics of lung clearance from pollutants, inhaled particles, and bacteria are adversely affected by exposure to tobacco smoke, by modifying the normal functions carried out by macrophages. The Drs. Masin are presently exploring the cytochemical differences in the macrophages of smokers and non-smokers.

Other special projects at the Sansum Foundation were concerned with fatty substances, the lipids, in cervical cells under hormonal stimulus, in cells of the urine and pulmonary cells and their possible significance in diagnosis of cancer in these particular organs. Extension of these studies is a current pilot project (1977) monitoring changes in urinary cells in cancer patients under chemotherapeutic treatment by alkylating agents for various types of malignancy. The Drs. Masin report substantial progress.

They are also studying cell patterns in the urine of patients suffering from cancer of the bladder, a type of carcinoma which can remain undetected for many years before the first alarming signals appear. Even if cystoscopic examinations are negative in asymptomatic patients, cells shed in the urine yield important clues to early diagnosis. From the characteristics of the nucleus of the malignant cell, from variations in its size, shape, and texture, the cytologist reads out the metabolic activity and state of differentiation of the malignant cell, and may predict the aggressiveness of the tumor.

A "flying spot television microscope" was built for the Masins at Los Angeles in 1960 and brought by them to Santa Barbara which enables them to study some properties of malignant cells by special techniques. Cells viewed on the television screen and simultaneously registered on an oscilloscope as pulse waves were evaluated for diagnostic purposes. Further automation of similar systems would obviously be of great value for economic cancer detection in large communities, an example of how discoveries made in Santa Barbara can accrue to the benefit of mankind.

Since 1956 the Drs. Masin have been known in the profession for their pioneering work with the fluorescence Acridine Orange method for diagnosis in exfoliated cytologic specimens. Their experience in this field has led at the present time to cooperation with Dr. J. W. Frost from Johns Hopkins University as consultants to the project for automation in sorting of pulmonary cells tagged by Acridine Orange as a fluorescent marker for nucleic acids, DNA and RNA.

In addition to the Masin's cancer research, Drs. Charles G. Chapman, Bernard J. Drury and James E. Hays have launched a study of lysosomal enzymes which could be used to assess the response of cancer patients to chemotherapy. Also, Dr. Drury and Dr. Edward J. McGinn are extending their studies of the effectiveness of new compounds in the treatment of several forms of arthritis, anticipating the Sansum Foundation's increased emphasis on arthritis research in future. Such studies have resulted in the availability of several new medicines which are bringing substantial relief to millions of arthritics.

The continuation and development of the Sansum Medical Research Foundation, as originally conceived by Dr. Sansum, is being spearheaded by his close friend and associate in the field of diabetes, Dr. Hildahl I. Burtness, the Foundation board chairman.

"Entering the 1960s our work was seriously impeded by lack of laboratory space," Dr. Burtness recalls. "I was determined that we should have a modern facility to honor Dr. Sansum's memory."

Dr. Burtness' dream was to be abundantly rewarded. Thanks to the gratitude of a celebrity diabetic who had been under his care for more than forty years, a new, ultramodern laboratory building was dedicated in 1966, to climax one of the more meaningful developments in the Sansum story.

16

The Bright Promise
of the Future

Harry W. Morrison, a resident of Boise, Idaho, was admitted to Cottage Hospital in 1932 suffering from severe diabetes. He became the patient of Dr. H. I. Burtness, and the lifelong friendship that evolved from this doctor-patient relationship was to yield profound benefits for the Sansum Medical Research Foundation.

Morrison, then 47, was co-founder of the Morrison-Knudson Company, Inc., one of the largest construction firms in the world. He was a contemporary of Warren Bechtel, one of Dr. Sansum's more famous diabetic patients. Mr. Morrison was fond of telling associates that so far as he was concerned, "Burt" Burtness was the world's best diabetes doctor. He was Dr. Burtness' patient for 40 years, often sending his private DC-3 aircraft, or later his DeHaviland executive jet, to fetch Dr. Burtness from Santa Barbara to Boise for "house calls."

Morrison was one of the world's major dam

builders. He had assisted Bechtel in forming the famous "Six Companies" to undertake the construction of Hoover Dam on the Colorado River, which Morrison followed with such projects as Bonneville Dam and a large portion of the Grand Coulee Dam, both on the Columbia River. His firm was co-builder of the bay bridge between Oakland and San Francisco. During World War II he built military installations from Midway, Wake and Pearl Harbor to Alaska and countless bases in the United States. His building projects were world-wide, as Dr. Burtness learned first-hand when he acompanied Morrison on a trip around the globe in 1963.

"Mr. Morrison visited Santa Barbara frequently for check-ups," Dr. Burtness said, "and took an active interest in the diabetes research we were doing at the Sansum Foundation. He began leaving $1,000 checks with the secretary, to be used for research purposes."

In the closing years of his life, Mr. Morrison and his second wife, the former Mrs. Velma V. Shannon of Bakersfield, announced that they would contribute $100,000 toward a laboratory building for the Sansum Foundation, with matching funds to be supplied by other donors.

The handsome two-level Harry and Velma Morrison Laboratory Building was completed in the spring of 1966, from designs by Robert Garland with the Joe Bailey Construction Company as general contractor. Located at 2219 Bath Street next to the Sansum Clinic and half a block south of Cottage Hospital, the building is reinforced concrete, with 6,000 square feet of floor space. The estate of Josephine Hanna provided $60,000 for equipment and furnishings.

Mr. and Mrs. Morrison were present at the dedication ceremonies of their new laboratory facility on June 9, 1966. The Foundation president, Dr. Burtness, presided, and the man responsible for bringing Dr. Sansum to Santa Barbara in 1920, Dr. Franklin R. Nuzum, delivered the dedicatory address. The director of laboratories, Dr. Domz, proudly informed the assemblage that "not one penny of federal money has gone into this building."

Harry Morrison was in his eighty-sixth year when he died in Boise on July 19, 1971, having survived severe diabetes for forty-one years. His widow Velma continues her interest and support of the research activities in Santa Barbara.

At long last, the Sansum Foundation researchers could move out of their cramped quarters in the Cottage Hospital. The Morrison building had been designed with second and third floors to be added at a later date when funding became available, to be used for heart, arthritis and allergy research. *

Full-scale diabetes research resumed in the Morrison Laboratories in July 1968 when Dr. Donald E. McMillan, a Stanford graduate born in San Francisco, joined the Sansum Foundation following a decade with the United States Public Health Service at various hospitals around the country. In 1963-65 he had been a fellow in endocrinology and metabolism at the University of California Medical Center in San Francisco. He held the rank of senior surgeon (commander) when he left government service to join the Sansum staff as director of diabetes research.

One of Dr. McMillan's principal discoveries in the field of diabetes research upon coming to Santa Barbara was that the blood of diabetics is for some reason more

---

* After occupying basement quarters for a decade, the development offices of the Sansum Foundation moved into a recently remodeled and renovated cottage next door to the Morrison Laboratory Building, thanks to Mr. and Mrs. Ray Klein of Santa Barbara whose gift was in memory of his father, Jacob Klein. This move released valuable space for additional medical research. Robert Bason heads the department of development for the Foundation.

viscous, or thicker, than the blood of non-diabetics. In laymen's language, this meant that the blood flow into capillaries and micro-blood vessels is impeded, resulting in dire complications in such areas of the body as the retina, causing blindness; the filtering system of the kidneys, causing nephritis; and the extremities, causing gangrene and the possibility of amputations. When the normal red corpuscle approaches the narrowing end of the circulatory system — the micro-capillaries — it has the capability of reducing its diameter by bending itself so as to be able to enter and move through a microscopic blood vessel. In diabetics, Dr. McMillan discovered, the corpuscles become rubbery and unyielding, causing a blockage at the entrance of a tiny capillary, thus shutting off the supply of blood to sustain life in areas beyond the point of blockage.

If Dr. McMillan and his staff succeed in determining the cause of this thickening of the blood in diabetics they will have struck a major blow at the complications of the disease, and possibly achieve, within one generation of Dr. Sansum's death, the founder's lifelong goal — a means of preventing diabetes itself.

"Such a goal is not beyond reach," Dr. McMillan says. "Just think back to what medical research has already done in relatively recent times. The age-old scourge of smallpox, the plague of the Middle Ages, is nearly extinct. Tuberculosis has been virtually conquered. Polio can be prevented. Artificial restorations of damaged joints have enabled thousands of arthritics to leave their wheelchairs and in many cases enjoy such activities as dancing and skating. Diphtheria epidemics are a thing of the past. Sooner or later man will find the answer to diabetes and cancer and arthritis. The answers lie in medical research."

Reporting in the *Journal of the American Diabetic Association* in 1976 on the subject of blood protein changes, blood viscosity and diabetic microangiopathy, Dr. McMillan wrote:

"Diabetic microangiopathy is a slowly progressive condition that usually manifests itself years after the onset of the carbohydrate-metabolism disturbance. It is far more striking in some diabetics than in others. Differences in the pattern of its effect in several body systems suggest that the local vascular disturbance is a mixture of a general microcirculatory change in diabetics, and a specific vascular alteration in each tissue. Its manifestations in the individual diabetic appear to be influenced by both elements.

"Evidence is presented that plasma protein changes in diabetics and their effects on blood flow play a role in accelerating the rate of progression of diabetic microangiopathy, by raising plasma viscosity and by increasing the affinity of erythrocytes for each other. The plasma protein change is dominated by a possibly hormonal mediated pattern of gammaglobulin elevation seen in many chronic disorders. This elevation of acute-phase proteins is not likely, by itself, to produce diabetic microangiopathy, but it may cause an additional stress on the metabolically disturbed diabetic microcirculation."

In June of 1977, scientists at UC San Francisco announced that they had successfully cloned the gene for insulin, making it possible for the first time anywhere to place the insulin gene into bacteria and make it reproduce itself in large quantities, using recombinant-DNA techniques.* Although genes from rats were used by the researchers, who are members of the UCSF Department of Biochemistry and Biophysics, they report that their work now makes it possible to clone human insulin genes in bacteria as well.

Mass production of human insulin in bacteria, the much-publicized goal of the highly controversial recombinant-DNA technology, would be a boon for diabetics who develop harmful allergic reactions to the beef and pig insulin now in use.

"Research is still required before it will be possible to make proteins like insulin from special DNA that has been added to bacteria," UCSF researchers report, "but the first step — putting the gene into bacteria — has now been accomplished for insulin."

The research with the rat insulin gene was supported in part by the National Institutes of Health, and is regarded as a medical break-through of the first magnitude.

The Sansum Medical Research Foundation, in keeping with hundreds of similar institutions around the world, stays in close touch with such developments in diabetes research elsewhere, exchanging knowledge in the highest sense of scientific endeavor. Some experimenters report projects that sound almost pseudoscientific, such as the recent announcement that a scientist was perfecting an "artificial pancreas," a metal and plastic device to be implanted in the human body, containing a six-month supply of insulin which would be injected into the tissues automatically whenever sensors detected a rise in blood sugar in the circulatory system. The insulin container would be

---

* DNA — deoxyribonucleic acid, part of the "spiral staircase" structure of the molecule of life.

refillable as needed through hypodermic injection from the outside. Considering the success and wide use of artificial pacemakers for the heart, an artificial pancreas no longer boggles the imagination.

In 1975 the Sansum Medical Research Foundation announced a four-year, four-phase campaign to raise $3,000,000 to support continuing research in the fields of diabetes, cancer, allergies, arthritis and heart disease.

Dr. Sansum's long-time friend and co-worker, Dr. Barkley S. Wyckoff, and Mrs. Velma Morrison are co-chairmen of the Hildahl I. Burtness Diabetic Research Fund, which has a quota of a million dollars. "Man's fulfillment calls for every resource to be used to its utmost to conquer disease today," they stated in a joint news release. "Failure to do so will beget a frightening heritage, multiplied by each generation in which progress is wanting. The Sansum Medical Research Foundation has the responsibility of fulfilling a course of events set in motion by Dr. William David Sansum more than fifty years ago."

Funds raised in the campaign would be used to step up the pace of research and provide for the much-needed new equipment required in this research, according to Dr. McMillan.

"In his quest for relief from pain and premature death," Dr. McMillan pointed out, "man has learned that substantial alleviation of suffering for millions is often achieved, not through dramatic breakthroughs, but through steadily-increasing knowledge which gradually reduces the total puzzle, piece by piece. Insulin has not cured diabetes, but consider the immensity of its benefits: elimination of certain death from diabetic coma, restoration of normal vigor, stamina, resistance to infection, and opportunity for normal careers and a fulfilling family life. Cures are not available for many diseases, but much is known about early detection and treatment, thanks to medical research in laboratories such as this one in Santa Barbara. The best hope for mankind lies in preventing disease, not in treating it after it comes. Research that adds to our preventive capabilities will enhance all our lives."

Phase Two of the Sansum Foundation's Fulfillment Program calls for one million dollars in support of cancer research, which is the only hope for countless victims of malignancies.

The third phase carries a goal of $750,000 to add two more floors to the Harry and Velma Morrison Research Laboratories, to provide for heart, arthritis and allergy research, the extra space deemed essential to achieve a full realization of linking research teams to the patients' bedsides.

"Medical research is noted for the virtuoso work of the Pasteurs, the Flemings and the Salks," Dr. Burtness reminded the public, "but it also includes the study of thousands of case histories on a given topic. Here in Santa Barbara the Foundation can bring more than 100,000 case histories to bear on a given problem."

In order to expand its research into the nation's number one killer, heart disease, and arthritis, the disease which causes more human misery than any other, the Sansum Foundation trustees added Phase Four to their program. It is an annual fund with a goal of $250,000 to support Sansum's ongoing research programs in those fields. Expansion of the physical plant under Phase Three would provide the necessary laboratories for cardiovascular, arthritis, and immunology research.

"The Board of Trustees has accepted the challenge that no promising avenue of research be dead-ended for lack of support," Dr. Domz said. "Funds must and will be found. Too many people are counting on us. While an 'annual fund' is not the most glamorous of needs, it is the very lifeline of continuing research at Sansum. Without annual support such as Dr. Sansum enjoyed in the formative years of his research work, the buildings and the men and women on the staff, and the sophisticated equipment, would stand idle."

The achievements of the Potter Metabolic Clinic and Sansum Research Foundation over a half century in Santa Barbara add up to an impressive list:

—The first among American advocates of taking diabetics off high-fat diets and placing them on more normal diets;

—Pioneering new methods of preparing insulin and extending its duration of action in the body;

—Work on cholesterol which was twenty years ahead in predicting cause-and-effect relationship between cholesterol and arteriosclerosis;

—Pioneering in the detection of cancer cells before a malignancy shows up as a lump or on X-ray film.

Throughout the country doctors recognize the urgency of further public education regarding the need to continue medical research. All too many otherwise well-informed people believe that the discovery of insulin, for example, ended the diabetes problem. Paradoxically, insulin increased the problem because it enabled diabetics to live into old age where they become highly susceptible to geriatric ailments.

In 1920, the year Dr. Sansum came to Santa Barbara, it was estimated by the Metropolitan Life Insurance Company that there were half a million people suffering from diabetes in the United States. The National Commission on Diabetes reported in 1976 that diabetes mellitus directly affected over ten million Americans! Between 1965 and 1975 the prevalence of diabetes increased by more than fifty per cent in the United States. More than 600,000 new cases are being diagnosed annually in this country — because diagnostic techniques are improving. According to the American Diabetes Association the incidence of diabetes is ballooning at a rate of six per cent annually, which means that the average American born today has better than one in five chances of becoming diabetic during his lifetime — unless a method of prevention is found. This is the goal and the challenge facing medical researchers.

A layman studying these alarming statistics might get the erroneous impression that medical research has lost ground to the disease since the discovery of insulin in 1921. What the layman may not realize is that in 1921 the diabetes census was low simply because victims of the disease died a few months after diagnosis. Today, thanks to medical research, diabetes patients are no longer doomed; most live out relatively normal lives. And precisely because diabetics are living longer, through insulin or diet control or both, the need for continuing medical research is more important than ever before.

Why this paradox? Because diabetics who live past middle age are twenty-five times more prone to blindness than are non-diabetics. They are seventeen times more prone to kidney disease, and five times more prone to gangrene. Diabetics are twice as vulnerable to heart disease than are non-diabetics; an estimated three out of four diabetics die of blood vessel diseases.

According to the American Diabetes Association, strong evidence presented to the Congressional Diabetes Commission indicates that diabetes and its complications are responsible for 300,000 deaths annually in the United States, a melancholy statistic which can be improved only through continuing research.

Equal in importance to the skill and dedication of our nation's medical researchers is the financial support of the average citizen. They are mutually dependent on each other. To acquaint prospective donors with the Sansum Medical Research Foundation's programs of fund raising, several ways to support the cause have been outlined in Foundation literature available at its central office of development at 2219 Bath Street, Santa Barbara 93105.

Robert E. Bason, director of development, lists the following alternatives for donors:

(1) Outright tax-deductible cash gifts;

(2) Real estate, which would enable the donor to avoid capital gains taxes;

(3) Securities;

(4) Personal property, such as rare books, antiques, art objects, paintings or the like, which are subject to similar tax advantages applicable to gifts of securities or appreciated properties;

(5) The new "Unitrust" created by the Tax Reform Act of 1969, whereby the donor can make a gift with substantial tax savings and at the same time retain income from the gift for the rest of his life and that of his spouse or other heirs;

(6) Annuity trusts;

(7) Insurance;

(8) Memorials.

"We have had a fine response from the public in our efforts to further research work at Sansum to date,"

Bason reports, "but the need is never-ending. Substantial contributions have been received from the Elizabeth Firth Wade Endowment Fund; the Robert Stewart Odell and Helen Pfeiffer Odell Fund; the Town and Country Women's Club of Santa Barbara; the Harry W. Morrison Family Foundation; the Morrison-Knudson Company of Boise, Idaho; the Moore Memorial Trust Fund of La Jolla; the Hearst Foundation of San Francisco and New York; the Edward T. Foley Foundation; Mr. and Mrs. James M. Richardson; the Apple Valley Foundation; the Builders' Concrete Corporation (via Glenn V. Stoner and Donald M. Underdown); Leon Strauss of San Francisco; Mr. and Mrs. Raymond L. Klein; Mr. Boone Gross; Mrs. Mildred Banderob, and the Dr. and Mrs. Joseph Fife Medical Research Fund, established by Dr. Fife's nephew and wife, Mr. and Mrs. William Fife, to support retinopathy research."

Between 1956 and 1977, bequests were received for research purposes from the following estates: Effie Bertlesen, Helen O'Brien, Chester Turner, Donalda Schneidt, Edith Seger, Elmer Clawson, Elizabeth Roberts Howland and Ora V. Hayward; and two annual bequests from the estates of Louise A. Bandy, Mary Josephine Hanna, Catherine Glenn and Helen Pauline Beardsley.

These donations were in addition to the support which the Sansum Foundation has received over the years from the Carnegie Corporation, the Fleischmann Foundation, the Damon Runyon Foundation, the American Cancer Society, the Kroc Foundation and the Doris Fay Palmer Trust, Bason emphasized.

The physical monuments to Dr. William David Sansum's memory are many, but the real monuments are not as obvious as the polished stone bearing his name at Santa Barbara Cemetery, or the impressive new home of the Sansum Medical Clinic which opened in

1976, or the Morrison Laboratories Building where Sansum's work goes on today. Rather, his memorial lies in the hearts and bodies of the uncounted thousands of diabetic patients who owe their lives to Dr. Sansum and the work he began as a medical student in Chicago in 1916.

Dr. H. I. Burtness, on whose shoulders fell the mantle of Dr. Sansum's lifelong crusade to conquer diabetes, sums it up this way:

"Sansum medical research has been over half a century in the coming and is now ready to fulfill the promise of its founder. What is to come tomorrow will not automatically follow any fifty-year period of advancement. We are now in the specific fifty-year segment which forms the arrowed tip of a 3,500-year medical thrust. Of all the fifty-year segments of the 3,500 years, the coming half century holds the greatest promise of achievement. Those years may well bring the long-sought answers to the prevention and cure of diabetes, cancer, arthritis and heart disease. The Sansum Medical Research Foundation, with its resources and tradition of achievement, is prepared to meet the challenge of these next five decades, as Dr. Sansum's continuing quest is projected into the Twenty-first Century."

THE END

Appendix:

Dr. Sansum's Publications

Extrasystoles in the Mammalian Heart due to Stimulation of the Keith Flack Node; Sansum, William D.; *Am. J. Physiol.* 1912.

Studies on the Theory of Diabetes, III. Glycolic Aldehyde in Phlorhizinized Dogs; Sansum, William D., and Woodyatt, R. T.; *J. Biol. Chem.* 17:521-527 (May) 1914.

Some Anaphylactic Reactions; Bradley, H. C., and Sansum, William D.; *J. Biol. Chem.* 18:497-507 (August) 1914.

Studies on the Theory of Diabetes, V. A Study of Narcotic Drugs in Phlorhizin Diabetes; Sansum, William D., and Woodyatt, R. T.; *J. Biol. Chem.* 21:1-22 (May) 1915.

Prolonged and Accurately Timed Intravenous Injections of Sugar. A Preliminary Report. Woodyatt, R. T., Sansum, William D., and Wilder, Russell M.; *J.A.M.A.* 65:2067-2070 (December 11) 1915.

The Use of Phlorhizinized Dogs to Determine the Utilizable Carbohydrate in Foods. The Food Value of Commercial Glucose. Sansum, William D., and Woodyatt, R. T.; *J. Biol. Chem.* 24:23-30 (January) 1916.

Studies on the Theory of Diabetes, VI. The Behavior of d-1-Glyceric Aldehyde in the Normal and Diabetic Organism. Sansum, William D., and Woodyatt, R. T.; *J. Biol. Chem.* 24:327-343 (March) 1916.

Studies on the Theory of Diabetes, VII. The Intravenous Tolerance Limit for d-1-Glyceric Aldehyde and the Improbability that it is a Chief Intermediate in Glucose Catabolism. Sansum, William D., and Woodyatt, R. T.; *J. Biol. Chem.* 24:343-347 (March) 1916.

Studies on the Theory of Diabetes, VIII. Timed Intravenous Injections of Glucose at Lower Rates. Sansum, William D., and Woodyatt, R. T.; *J. Biol. Chem.* 30:155-174 (May) 1917.

d-Glucose Tolerance in Health and Disease; Wilder, Russell M., and Sansum, William D.; *Arch. Int. Med.* 19:311-334 (February) 1917.

Rapid Reduction of Intraocular Tension in Glaucoma; By Timed Intravenous Glucose Injections. Sansum, William D.; *J.A.M.A.* 68:1885-1888 (June 23) 1917.

The Treatment of Diabetes Mellitus. A Brief Outline on the Management of Typical Moderately Severe Cases of Diabetes Mellitus for the Use of Patients, Social Workers, Students and Physicians in the Central Free Dispensary, Located at Rush Medical College, Chicago. Sansum, William D. Chicago. July 1, 1918. Booklet.

The Principles of Treatment in Mercuric Chlorid Poisoning. An Experimental Study. Sansum, William D.; *J.A.M.A.* 70:824-828 (March 23) 1918.

The Influence of Forced Diuresis in Experimental Poisoning with Diphtheria Toxin; Sansum, William D.; *J.A.M.A.* 70:904, 905 (March 30) 1918.

The Treatment of Constipation; Sansum, William D.; *M. Clin. N. America* 3:175-189 (July) 1919.

Fever and the Water Reserve of the Body; Balcar, J. O., Sansum, William D., and Woodyatt, R. T.; *Arch. Int. Med.* 24:116-128 (July) 1919.

The Preparation of Sugar-Free Cream for Diabetic Patients; Smith, Florence H., and Sansum, William D.; *J.A.M.A.* 76:792, 793 (March 19) 1921.

Further Studies on the Nature of Fever: Schmitt, E. C., and Sansum William D.; *California State J. Med.* 19:371 (September) 1921.

Potter Metabolic Clinic of Santa Barbara Cottage Hospital; Sansum, William D.; *Mod. Hosp.* 17:264 (October) 1921.

A Simple Method for the Washing of Bran for Diabetic Diets; Smith, Florence H., and Sansum, William D.; *California State J. Med.* 20:194-198 (June) 1922.

Treatment of Diabetes with Insulin ; Sansum, William D., and others; *J. Metab. Research* 3:641-676 (May-June) 1923.

Treatment of Severe Diabetes Complicated by Severe Tuberculosis with Insulin; Sansum, William D.; *Am. Rev. Tuberc.* 7:375-385 (August) 1923.

The Use of Basic Diets in the Treatment of Nephritis; Sansum, William D., Blatherwick, Norman R., and Smith F. H.; *J.A.M.A.* 81:883-886 (September 15) 1923.

Sources of Error in Organotherapy as Illustrated by Preparation and Administration of Insulin; Sansum, William D., and Blatherwick, Norman R.; *Endocrinology* 7:661-669 (September-November) 1923.

The Essential Points in the Treatment of Diabetes with Insulin; Sansum, William D., and Blatherwick, Norman R.; *California State J. Med.* 21:420-423 (October) 1923.

Insulin, Its Discovery and Use; Sansum, William D.; *Hosp. and Nurses Rev.*; p. 107, 1923.

A Case Report of the Clinical Findings and the Results Obtained in the Treatment of a Severe Case of Diabetes by the Proven Endocrine Substance, Insulin; Sansum, William D.; *Endocrinology* 8:103-105 (January) 1924.

The Present Status of the Treatment of Diabetes with Insulin; Sansum, William D., and others; *California and West. Med.* 22:321-323 (July) 1924.

The Absorption of Insulin from the Alimentary Canal; Maxwell, L. C., Blatherwick, Norman R., and Sansum, William D.; *Am. J. Physiol.* 70:351-257 (October) 1924.

The Insulin Requirement on Various Diets; Blatherwick, Norman T., Sansum, William D., Bell, Marion, and Hill, Elsie; *J. Metab. Research*, Vols. 7, 8, Nos. 1-6:39-49, January 1925-December 1926.

The Experimental Production of Hypertension: Nuzum, Franklin R., Osborne, M., and Sansum, William D.; *Arch. Int. Med.* 35:492-499 (April) 1925.

Lard and Laziness; Sansum, William D., and Bowden, Ruth; *Better Health*, Vol. 7, No. 1: (January) 1926.

The Use of High Carbohydrate Diets in the Treatment of Diabetes Mellitus; Sansum, William D., Blatherwick, Norman R., and Bowden, Ruth; *J.A.M.A.* 86:178-181 (January 16) 1926.

Safe Reducing Diets. I Reduce — A Department for the Would-Be-Thin Readers of Hygeia. Sansum, William D.; *Hygeia:* 147, 148 (March) 1926.

Safe Reducing Diets. Pointing Out the Dangers in Reducing Weight and Showing How to Avoid Them. Sansum, William D., and Bowden, Ruth; Western Dietitian 1: (July) 1926.

Enteric-coated Pancreatin Tablets as an Aid to Digestion; Sansum, William D.; *The Therapeutic Gazette, Whole Series*, Vol. 1, No, 7; Third Series, Vol. XLII: (July 15) 1926.

Normal Diet Menus. Sansum, William D., and Bowden, Ruth; *Western Dietitian:* (January) 1927.

Acidosis. How Foods May be Effectively Used in its Prevention and Cure with Menus. Sansum, William D., and Bowden, Ruth; *Food Facts* (formerly *Western Dietitian*): (May) 1927.

The Cause and Treatment of Constipation; Sansum, William D., and Bowden, Ruth; *Food Facts* 3:7-35 (September 15) 1927.

The Use of High Carbohydrate Diets in the Treatment of Diabetes Mellitus; Sansum, William D.; *Colorado Med.* 24:307-313 (October) 1927.

Training Diets; Sansum, William D., and Bowden, Ruth; *Food Facts:* (November) 1927.

The Ethmoidal and Sphenoidal Sinuses as Sources of Focal Infection; Sansum, William D.; *Radiology* 9:410-414 (November) 1927.

Diets for Expectant and Nursing Mothers; Sansum, William D.; *California and West. Med.* 28:33-38 (January) 1928.

219

Indigestion; Sansum, William D.; *Food Facts:* (January) 1928.

Better Breakfast; Sansum, William D.; *Food Facts:* 1928.

The Part Fruit Plays in the Diet; Sansum, William D., and Bowden, Ruth; *The Modern Priscilla:* (January) 1929.

The Use of Normal Diets in the Treatment of Diabetes; Treament of Mild Cases of Diabetes. Sansum, William D., Gray, Percival A., and Bowden, Ruth; *West. Hosp. and Nurses Rev.* 13:27 (January) 1929.

Achlorhydria Gastrica; A Simple Management. Preliminary Report on 50 Cases. Sansum, William D., and Gray, Percival A., Jr.; *California and West. Med.* 30:221-225 (April) 1929.

Phenylhydrazine Poisoning. Report of a Case. McNamara, Delbert H., and Sansum, William D.; *J.A.M.A.* 96:268,269 (January 24) 1931.

An Unusual Effect of Carbohydrate-Rich, Fat-Poor Diabetic Diet. Report of a Case. Gray, Percival A., and Sansum, William D.; *Endocrinology* 15:234-236 (May-June) 1931.

Diabetic Coma with Marked Hyperglycemia and Recovery. Report of a Case. Gray, Percival A., and Sansum, William D.; *J.A.M.A.* 97:230 (July 25) 1931.

A Comparative Study of Rabbits Maintained on Barley or Alfalfa; Bischoff, Fritz, Sansum, William D., Long, M. Louisa, and Evans, Richard D.; *J. Nutrition* 5:403-411 (July) 1932.

The Treatment of Indigestion, Underweight and Allergy, with Old and New Forms of Digestive Agents; Sansum, William D.; *Southwestern Med.* 16:452-462 (November) 1932.

The Diet in Diabetes; Gray, Percival A., and Sansum, William D.; *Diabetes 1:* (January) 1933.

The Higher Carbohydrate Diet Method in Diabetes Mellitus. Analysis of 1,005 Cases. Gray, Percival A., and Sansum, William D.; *J.A.M.A.* 100:1580-1584 (May 20) 1933.

On Obesity. Dangers and Treatment. Sansum, William D.; *California and West. Med.* 41:1-8 (December) 1934.

The Calcium and Phosphorus Requirements of the Body with Special Reference to Dental Nutrition; Sansum, William D. Read at Alumni Assn. Convention, College of Dentistry, Univ. Southern California, Feb. 4, 1935.

The Favorable Influence of Adequate (Higher) Carbohydrate Diets on the Blood Pressure of Diabetic Patients; Sansum, William D.; *South. M. J.* 29:414-417 (April) 1936.

Treatment of Diabetes Mellitus with Insoluble Insulin Compounds; II. Histone-Insulin. Gray, Percival A., Bischoff, Fritz, and Sansum, William D.; *Ann. Int. Med.* 11:274-284 (August) 1937.

The Favorable Influence of Adequate (Higher) carbohydrate, Lower Fat Diets on Arteriosclerosis Problem Associated with Diabetes Mellitus; Sansum, William D.; *Acta med. Scandinav.*, Supp. 90, pages 80-86, 1938. (Special edition presented to Dr. Hagedorn of Copenhagen, on his birthday, 1938).

The Present Treatment of Diabetes Mellitus; Sansum, William D.; *J. Am. Dietet. A.* 16:407-415 (May) 1940.

Diabetes Mellitus; Some of the Newer Factors in its Etiology and Treatment. Sansum, William D.; *California and West.Med.* 60: 13-18 (January) 1944.

The Importance of a Normal Blood Sugar in the Prevention and Treatment of Diabetes; Sansum, William D.: *ADA Forecast* 2:9-12 (January) 1949. Written a short time before the death of Dr. Sansum and published in *ADA Forecast* as a last message from a renowned doctor.

A Thirty-Fifth Anniversary of Insulin Therapy and a Sixty-Fifth Wedding Anniversary; Burtness, Hildahl I., and Cain, E. F.: *Diabetes* 7:59-61 (January-February) 1958.

The Miraculous Life of Charles E. Cowan; Burtness, Hildahl I.; *ADA Forecast* 11:1-3 (May-June) 1958.

BOOKS

Instructions to Diabetic Patients. Sansum, William D., Bowden, Ruth, and Berger, John. Schauer Printing Studio, Santa Barbara, Calif. 1926.

The Normal Diet. Sansum, William D. St. Louis. C. V. Mosby Company. Second Ed., revised. August, 1927.

The Treatment of Diabetes Mellitus with Higher Carbohydrate Diets. Sansum, William D., Gray, Percival A., and Bowden, Ruth. Harper. 1929.

Caloric Requirements. The Cyclopedia of Medicine [Piersol], pp. 31-35. Sansum, William D., Gray, Percival A., and Bowden, Ruth. Copyright F. A. Davis Company. Philadelphia, 1930.
Revised. Sansum, William D., and Bowden, Ruth. 1946.
Revised. Bowden, Ruth. 1952.

The Normal Diet and Healthful Living. Sansum, William D., Hare, R. A., and Bowden, Ruth. The Macmillan Company. 1936.

Manual for Diabetic Patients. Sansum, William D., Koehler, Alfred E., and Bowden, Ruth. The Macmillan Company. 27 pages. 1939.